LIFE SCIENCE LIBRARY

WHEELS

LIFE SCIENCE LIBRARY

WHEELS

by Wilfred Owen, Ezra Bowen
and the Editors of TIME-LIFE BOOKS

CONSULTING EDITORS

René Dubos
Henry Margenau
C. P. Snow

TIME-LIFE INTERNATIONAL (NEDERLAND) B.V.

ABOUT THIS BOOK

OF ALL MAN'S MECHANICAL INVENTIONS, none has changed his way of living so drastically as the wheel. So great has been its impact that the technological progress of civilizations can be measured in terms of the uses they have made of wheeled vehicles. This volume surveys that progress from the solid wheeled ox-carts of ancient times to the 130-m.p.h. Shinkansen express and turbine-powered trucks. It traces the many turns of the wheel's development, and points to innovations that are likely to shape human society in the future.

The text chapters are supplemented by picture essays. For example, Essay 2, "An Iron Horse on Tracks of Steel", augments Chapter 3, which surveys the development of railways from the early steam-engines to the latest diesel locomotive. Essay 7, "Cities without Congestion", is concerned with imaginative solutions to problems of urban travel posed in the chapter that goes before it.

THE AUTHORS

WILFRED OWEN is the Director of the Transportation Research Program for the Brookings Institution in Washington, D.C. During the Kennedy Administration he served as the director of a special task force on transport policy in the Department of Commerce. He has served also as a member of the World Bank's Economic Mission to India, the Harvard Advisory Service to Pakistan and the United Nations Economic Commission for Asia and the Far East, and has made special studies of American and European transportation problems for the Twentieth-Century Fund. His books include *Strategy for Mobility*, *The Metropolitan Transportation Problem* and *Distance and Development*.

EZRA BOWEN, formerly an editor for SPORTS ILLUSTRATED, is an assistant managing editor of TIME-LIFE BOOKS. He was series editor of *This Fabulous Century* and *The Old West*, and is author of *The High Sierra* in The American Wilderness series.

THE CONSULTING EDITORS

RENÉ DUBOS, a member and professor emeritus of The Rockefeller University, is a distinguished microbiologist and experimental pathologist who was awarded the Arches of Science Award in 1966 and the Pulitzer Prize in 1969 for his book *So Human an Animal: How We Are Shaped by Surroundings and Events*. He also authored *Mirage of Health* and *Man Adapting* and co-authored *Health and Disease* in this series.

HENRY MARGENAU is Eugene Higgins Professor Emeritus of Physics and Natural Philosophy at Yale, and an authority in spectroscopy and nuclear physics. He wrote *Open Vistas* and *The Nature of Physical Reality*, and is co-author of *The Scientist* in this series.

C. P. SNOW has won an international audience for his novels, including *The New Men*, *The Affair* and *Corridors of Power*, which explore the effects of science on today's society.

Authorised British edition © 1967, 1975, Time-Life International (Nederland) B.V.
Original English language edition published in United States by © Time Inc. 1965.
All rights reserved.

CONTENTS

PREFACE

THIS BOOK is more than a history of the wheel. It is also a perceptive account of the interrelationship between transportation and the economic and social progress of the human race.

From the primitive carts of antiquity to the complex vehicles and transport systems of today, the authors trace the evolution of land travel. Over the centuries, new technologies have extended the range of what man could do on and with the wheel, that basic and simple device. Improved families of vehicles and new sources of motive power have been combined with a variety of travelled ways—roads, rails, bridges and even subways—to complete the elements necessary to systems of transportation. These attempts to reduce the "friction of space" succeeded in increasing speed and lowering the effort and cost of movement for man and his goods. At times, new conditions of travel have opened up vast opportunities for man to embrace new ways of living and of making a living.

Today, while enjoying the fastest and most comprehensive transportation facilities the world has ever seen, we encounter new challenges and limitations. Some critical segments of these systems are inefficient, overburdened, obsolescent. To supersede them, transportation planners and designers are thinking not only in terms of many new kinds of "hardware" (the roadways, vehicles and the like) but also are working on the "software" (the data processing, analytical methods and operational control schemes) by which the separate hardware elements may be made to serve as effective composite systems.

We are finding that restrictions on the availability of energy and the need to protect the environment require a fresh approach to transportation planning. We are coming to the view that, especially in our great urban regions, the structuring of the region must go hand in hand with the provision of the means of movement, and transportation must consist of a co-ordinated mix of modes and services suited to the kind of society it is to serve.

—HARMER E. DAVIS

Director Emeritus of the Institute of Transportation
and Traffic Engineering
University of California

1

This Rolling
World

Streamers of car lights outline a web-like interchange at Sixth and Seventh Streets on the
Harbor Freeway in Los Angeles, California, a
city where the motor-car, the world's major ex-
ploitation of the wheel, is an essential of life.

IN THE HILL COUNTRY north-east of Osaka, the steel wheels of the Shinkansen express sing a song of triumphant speed as they whirl over the rails, carrying the world's fastest scheduled train through the mist of a Japanese morning. Three hours and 10 minutes after leaving Osaka, the thousand passengers aboard will pull into Tokyo, 320 miles away. Average speed: over 100 m.p.h., with only two stops and not a single level crossing.

Over a rutted track outside the Indian city of Ludhiana, the wooden wheels of a bullock cart squeak and rumble in the night. The driver is headed home to a little village called Sehora. In an hour or so, he will be there. Average speed: three miles an hour, not much faster than Indian farmers moved when they first began to use wheels like these over 4,000 years ago.

At the edge of Houston, an air-conditioned sedan provides welcome creature comfort as its driver rolls to work over the smooth, concrete surface of the Gulf Freeway. The highway is crowded—about 5,500 cars and lorries in one hour on a six-mile stretch—but the traffic flows quite smoothly. At a central control room, a Houston police officer scans a bank of closed-circuit television screens, alert for stalled cars and accidents. Near by, computers clock traffic and adjust signals at entrance ramps to control the number of cars funnelled on to the Freeway. Speed at rush hour: a little over 30 miles per hour. Later, when crowds ease off, speed is held to a minimum of 40 m.p.h. and a maximum of 50 m.p.h.

All over the world, by day and by night, hundreds of millions of other wheels are rolling across the land, bearing the traffic of the human race. Some of the wheels, like those on the Gulf Freeway or the Shinkansen line, spin to the swift rhythm of 20th-century technology, carrying the mainstream of the modern world on its hurrying course. Others, like those of the wooden cart on the dusty road outside Sehora, turn to the slow tempo of antiquity, and by so doing they have stranded their villages and their nations in a backwater of primitive technology and culture, a backwater in which more than half the world's population is still languishing. For the impact of the wheel—which has governed man's progress from the immobility of the Stone Age to the mobility of modern society—is still being felt today in every corner of the earth. Wherever the wheel is and however slowly or fast it turns, the wheel's pace is the pace of mankind. In fact, there is no surer measure of a nation's progress than the measure of its system of transportation, and the speed with which it can move people and products from place to place.

In the United States in 1970 there were over 100 million cars, lorries and buses—nearly one motor vehicle for every two people in the nation. Their wheels roll across some three million miles of surfaced roads, including nearly 70,000 miles of multi-lane highways. As they turn, these motor wheels and those of about 31,000 engines and 1.8 million railway coaches moving over some 200,000 miles of railway line affect the lives of every American. After 1840, the U.S. grew up the way it did because of wheels: the nation expanded beyond the Mississippi in wagons and railway coaches; the American city was nurtured at a railhead; the city spread outwards in trolley cars and Model T Fords; and now the megalopolis is growing beyond conscience and almost beyond control because of the mobility of the modern motor-car.

In the U.S. today nearly everything a man uses rolls on rails or over a highway at some time or other. Ninety-seven per cent of all milk, about seventy per cent of all fruits and vegetables in leading markets, and almost every stitch of clothing sold in the country arrives at the store in a lorry. Schools have been dramatically changed by the motor vehicle: since the first school bus appeared, 225,000 one-room schoolhouses have been supplanted by bigger, better, central schools. When the children attending those schools grow up, there is a fair chance their jobs will depend on the motor-car or the business it creates: 75 per cent of the nation's plate glass goes into motor vehicles, about 70 per cent of all rubber used, and over 40 per cent of all radios.

Add to this immense whirl of automotive activity the workhorse service of the U.S. railway system in handling more than 850,000 million ton-miles per year of inter-city freight: some 1,600,000 vans of grain, 375 million tons of coal and 110 million tons of forest products move over the rails.

Rolling into trouble

In all, the wheels and roadways of America have given the nation a greater potential for mobility than any other country has ever known, and with it, a higher standard of productivity and prosperity. But even with this wealth of transportation technology, the wheels of America are not rolling as smoothly as they might. Traffic has become so bad all over the U.S. that even in a city like Cedar Rapids, Iowa (population: 103,000), the average trip across town—seven miles—can take 45 minutes during rush hours. Outside Los Angeles on one farcical though mercifully non-fatal morning, 150 cars crunched together in accidents on the Santa Ana and Harbor Freeways. Other days the drivers are not so lucky: in the last 25 years motor vehicles have killed one million Americans.

The railways present a different kind of problem. Sixty years ago the railways provided a fast, efficient way to transport people and goods over land. Inter-city passengers rode de luxe expresses which sometimes thundered along at 70 m.p.h. on the main runs; freight rumbled for hundreds of miles between cities at 25 m.p.h. for a 35-coach train. At the time, after 50 centuries of plodding animal transport, travellers found the speed and power of the railway to be little short of miraculous. But today, while other forms of transportation leap into new dimensions of technological achievement, many railways still rattle along with such dreary, old equipment that in the 1960's the President of the United States, Lyndon B. Johnson, was moved to comment, "We have airplanes which fly three times faster than sound. We have television cameras that are orbiting Mars. But we have the same tired and inadequate mass transportation between our towns and cities that we had 30 years ago". And in fact, the average speed on one rail commuter run actually decreased by 30 per cent over six decades.

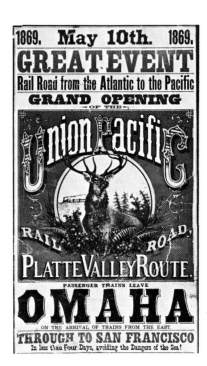

A NATION-SPANNING RAILWAY was proclaimed in posters throughout the eastern United States in 1869, and four other transcontinental lines were in use within 25 years. Together they opened up the West. Given more than 130 million acres of land along their routes by the U.S. federal government, the railways became zealous colonizers. Their agents advertised in cities for settlers, recruited farmers from among the immigrants arriving on the piers of New York, and even went to Europe to sell railway tickets into America's heartland.

What ails American wheels has been summed up by Harmer Davis, former head of the Institute of Transportation and Traffic Engineering at the University of California: "In the past, the study of transportation has been conducted haphazardly on a relatively small scale and rarely in terms of overall problems". Another transport expert, at the Massachusetts Institute of Technology, has observed, "The thing to understand is that about three decades ago the real story of the wheel stopped being just the linear evolution of separate lines of technology". The challenge now is to weave those lines together into a carpet of mobility on which the goods and people of the nation can move at speeds which reflect the tempo of the jet age rather than the era of steam.

Rolling into the future

To meet this challenge, extensive research and demonstration projects, backed by tens of millions of dollars in government money, have been undertaken, aimed at developing the world's first complete system of transportation. The system may include a Shinkansen-type train, a TV-monitored highway, a computer-controlled traffic system, a freight yard with similar computer control, or sealed freight containers which can be transloaded from trucks to trains to planes to ships in minutes with virtually no manhandling. "The freight vehicle of the future", says one transport authority, "may be no more than a platform on wheels." Beyond such existing technology, the system may also breed brand-new kinds of guideways, operational controls and vehicles, some of which may have no wheels at all.

But far more important than any single line of technology will be the system itself, a co-ordinated network in which motor vehicles, trains, ships and aeroplanes each handles its own proper segment of the transportation load; in which every mode of transport feeds smoothly into the next, instead of scrabbling around in an inefficient tangle of redundant services, traffic jams and obsolescent machinery.

While the U.S. is looking for a radically new system of transportation to match the demands of the space age, nations like India, Pakistan, Thailand, Colombia and China, embracing two-thirds of the world's people, are trying to create a basic pattern of mobility which will allow them to feed and educate their people, to develop a modern industrial society and, in effect, to rise out of the mire of antiquity in which many of their people still languish. Without their fair share of wheels and roadways, none of these things can be done. In Africa, there are only about 50,000 miles of railway track, and those few miles are chopped up into nine different rail gauges, so there is no way for the same train to get across the continent or in some instances even from one country to another. In Thailand, with 2,170 miles of track, the train from Bangkok to Chiangmai is pulled through the forests and rice fields by a wood-burning locomotive.

In Mexico, there is one motor vehicle for every 30 people, and the classic form of transportation in many rural areas is still the burro. In

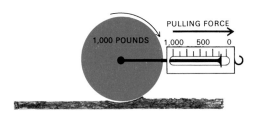

THE WHEEL'S ADVANTAGE rests in the low friction it encounters. As it turns (*above*), it must roll upwards against a small hill of ground that it squeezes up ahead of it. This resistance, called rolling friction, is much less than that of an object dragged over the ground. To keep a 1,000-pound load on a crude wooden wheel moving, only about 80 pounds of pulling force is needed (as indicated by the scale beside the wheel). The heavier resistance encountered by a load when it is dragged over the ground (*below*) is caused by the partial interlocking of microscopic irregularities on the surfaces of the load and the ground. This resistance—called sliding friction—is so much larger than rolling friction that a pulling force of about 400 pounds is needed to drag a 1,000-pound wooden load over the ground.

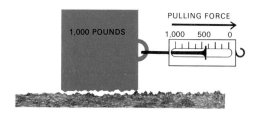

Kashmir a truck is held in such awe that it is likely to carry a metal plaque with the word *Shaktiman*, meaning "all powerful". In Pakistan, despite the conglomeration of diesel trucks, Fords, Volkswagens, bicycles, hand carts and two-wheeled, horse-driven tongas, the national vehicle is still the bullock-cart. And a bullock-cart cannot carry a man or his produce or his horizons much beyond the limits of his village. Only 11 per cent of the 570,000 rural villages of India are connected to the rest of the country by all-weather roads. In a village in the state of Madhya Pradesh, no one would volunteer to distribute the local rice ration because the roads were so bad. In this same town, an old man remarked, "We almost never see a stranger in our village, and so we do not know what is going on outside". Even courtship is held up by poor transportation: a man who lives on a bad road often cannot get a good wife because the parents of the bride refuse to slog through the mud to visit after the marriage.

This struggle for mobility which is going on all over the world today is the same struggle for mobility that men have carried on for 10,000 years. And in most places, the battle is being fought with the weapons of the past. The technology of Thailand's wood-burning locomotive dates from the 1850's. The bullock-cart of Sehora was rolling at the time of Christ. And the burro ambling down a mountain trail in Mexico is, in essence, the same animal that sweated under its burden on the plains of Egypt thousands of years ago, before there were any wheels in the world.

Those days when there were no wheels were desperately slow days, and they occupied most of human history. A man's mobility was provided by his feet. His radius for a day's travel, out and back, was about 15 to 20 miles. And the heaviest load he could carry on his back for any distance was about 90 pounds. About the fifth millennium B.C., he trained his first beast of burden. Probably it was an ass, possibly it was an ox. In either case, by strapping a load on to the animal, he was able to move three times the 90 pounds he could carry any distance on his own back. Next he took the burden off the ox and put it on to a land sledge, a crude platform with heavy wooden runners. A pair of oxen, hitched to the sledge by a yoke and pole, could pull upwards of 3,000 pounds. This was more like it. But still there had to be a better way.

Birth of the wheel

And one day it appeared. On the fertile delta of the Tigris and Euphrates, some time in the fourth millennium B.C., an unknown Sumerian produced what must surely be man's greatest single technological achievement. He made a wheel. Precisely who he was or how he planned to use it will never be known. He may have been a warrior putting together the first war chariot. Or he may have been a mourner providing a smoother ride for some particularly esteemed corpse. The earliest record of a vehicular wheel is a sketch made by an accountant in Sumer about 3500 B.C. The vehicle was apparently a funeral wagon, a bizarre contraption with an undercarriage that swooped up in front like the runners of old-fashioned ice skates, indicating that this wagon may have been an immediate offspring of the land sledge. The upper body was a tall box on end with a peaked roof. Underneath, there were two pairs of unmistakable wheels. They were probably about two feet in diameter, made of slabs of wood fastened together by cross-pieces and then rounded off as carefully as the primitive copper tools of the day would permit. Both axles were fixed rigidly in place. Since the front axle could swing to neither left nor right for a turn, the wagon had to be skidded or lifted around corners.

A blow to friction

The technology of these first wheels was not very elegant. Nevertheless, they mechanized the Sumerian way of death, and in so doing gave the world a new dimension in mobility. All of a sudden man's ability to move things over land was no longer limited by his capacity—or an animal's—to carry a weight of cargo on his back, or to slither it along on a sledge.

By making the first vehicular wheel, that ingenious Sumerian created a number of things. In scientific terms, he had created a passive roller, an instrument for reducing surface friction in the movement of loads over land. In the days before wheels, a pair of oxen pulling a 3,000-pound load on a sledge had to exert about 1,200 pounds of pull to overcome the surface friction between the ground and the load. A wheel can cut this friction between the ground and the load as much as 100 times. And in fact, with a wheel as round and hard as a railway train wheel, moving over a surface as smooth and hard as a rail, 9 pounds of effort will easily keep 3,000 pounds of load in motion. But those first wooden wheels were neither very round nor very hard. Besides, on a dirt surface the wheel sank in and was always running a little uphill. Despite these imperfections, in time, when wheels and axles and wagons could be built strong enough, a good wheel pulled by a pair of stout oxen could move at least two or three times the load that the same team could move with a land sledge.

In far broader terms, along with the wheel, the Sumerians inadvertently created something else. They put together the beginnings of the first modern system of land transportation. That first wheel, mounted beneath a primitive cart, pulled by a pair of oxen down that rough dirt roadway, carried something—in that earliest version, only a corpse—from one place to another more efficiently than that particular item had ever been carried before. This is what wheels were all about when they were first invented. And this is what they are still about today: the vital element in a fascinating and complex thing called a system of transportation. In time, as man improved the technology of wheels and engines, he would find that there were almost no limits to the weight his wheels could carry, or the speeds with which they could be made to turn. However, he would be many long years and many long miles in bringing them to their full potential.

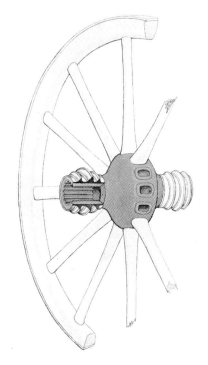

A PRIMITIVE ROLLER BEARING, found in Denmark with other parts of a first-century B.C. funeral wagon, is one of the refinements that made Celtic wheels the finest to have been developed in ancient times. The bearing, which served to reduce the friction between the moving hub of a wheel and the fixed axle, was an outward extension of the single-piece oak hub (*blue, above*), and was lined on the inside with semicircular grooves. Each of these grooves contained a small wooden roller (*detail, below*) which rotated as the wheel turned, enabling the wheel to roll on the axle instead of scraping around it.

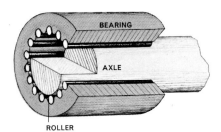

About the year 2000 B.C., several tribes from the steppes near the Black Sea appeared in the Tigris-Euphrates Valley with a strange, fast animal called the horse. Along with it they brought a spoked wheel, greater in diameter and therefore able to roll more easily over rough terrain than the average solid wheel, and far lighter and more manœuvrable. Other tribes adopted the new technology: the Philistines, the Egyptians, the peoples of Babylon, Greece and China.

The wheels of antiquity reached their technological peak in the Roman Empire—not in Rome itself but among the Celts of Western Europe. The Celtic wagon makers were superb. Their vehicles were the first to have swivelling front axles, which could swing left or right in a turn. To reduce friction inside their wheel hubs, the Celts installed hardwood rollers, so that the wheels no longer scraped their way around the axle but rolled on bearings which in turn rolled on the axle. Radiating outwards from the hubs were as many as 14 slender spokes mortised into a felloe, or rim, made of a single piece of heat-bent ash. The tyres, too, were in a single piece—strips of iron joined together and hammered into a hoop that was completed by welding the ends. The iron tyre was built a shade smaller in diameter than the felloe, then heated and fitted on while still hot. When the iron cooled, the tyre shrank, locking all the parts of the wheel together.

Basic improvement

In terms of basic technology, these Celtic wagons were almost as good as an animal-drawn wagon would ever need to be. Looking back at this early climax in animal-powered mobility, the scholar Gregory of Nyssa commented gratefully, "It was the slowness and difficult motion of our body that brought the horse to supply our need [and] the ox to render service to our life, who makes our living easy for us by his own labour".

Though his gratitude may have been well placed, Gregory had not much grasp of the economics of animal-drawn wheels. The ancient ox-cart moved at one and a half miles an hour. The horse could pull a cart a little faster, but not for long. The horse harness of antiquity was merely a modified version of the ox's yoke with neck- and bellyband. And while this arrangement rested comfortably against an ox's heavy, angular shoulders, on a horse the neckband would pull back to press against the animal's windpipe and jugular whenever it pulled a load. As a result, over-land movement of bulk cargo was so slow and uncertain that the cost of a load of grain doubled for every hundred miles it travelled. No one who lived more than 30 miles—two days' travel—from a major market or water port could afford to grow any surplus crops, or produce any surplus products for sale. And so, most rural people still existed at a bare subsistence level.

Finally, in the ninth century A.D., the Franks under Charlemagne discovered how to get the most out of a draught horse. They began to use a rigid horse collar, which rested against the horse's withers so that the animal could pull against it comfortably with its full strength.

Now, at last, a team of horses could pull a decent load—as much as any pair of oxen. Furthermore, they could pull it almost twice as fast as before, covering at least 25 miles a day instead of 15. And with iron shoes, which became common by the 11th century, the horse would be less likely to come up lame after a long day's journey. With more efficient horse-power, the price of a wagon-load of grain rose only 30 per cent per 100 miles, the price of a load of wool but 3 per cent. Now there was an incentive to grow a surplus. Production in the fields of Western Europe rose as much as 40 per cent per man, and the peasants who had lived in tiny 5- or 10-house hamlets scattered all over the rural landscape began to move into bigger central towns: because of the speed of their horse-drawn wagons, they could travel each day to a distant field and still get home by dark. "Thus, in time, Mechanics . . . progressed further," wrote Guidobaldo del Monte in 1577, in one of his *Six Books of Mechanics*, "and with carts and carriages conveyed provisions, wares and all kinds of heavy loads between neighbouring peoples, and then brought necessities to us from their place of origin."

Common flaw

In the centuries that followed, these medieval carts and wagons were supplanted by waves of efficient, stronger, lighter, more elegant horse-drawn vehicles: the Conestoga freight wagons and the Concord stage-coaches with their lever brakes; the dashing cabriolets; the ubiquitous buggies with their elliptical springs for soft riding; the buckboards (the pick-up lorries of their day); the handsome victorias; the gigs, shays, traps, landaulets, runabouts, calashes and curricles. Each had its own use, and each in its way was an effort to make the wheel a better instrument of transportation. But all shared two common flaws: they were all pulled by an engine called a horse, and they all ran on a dirt track or, at best, a gravel road. As late as 1817, it still took 50 days to move freight from Cincinnati to New York, a distance of under 700 miles. A U.S. Senate committee complained in 1816: "A coal mine may exist in the U.S. not more than 10 miles from valuable ores of iron and other materials, and both of them be useless . . . as the price of land carriage is too great to be borne by either". The fastest recorded time for a stage-coach on the 222-mile trip from Frederick, Maryland, to Wheeling, West Virginia, over the relatively superb gravelled surface of the Cumberland Road, then the best highway in the nation, was $23\frac{1}{2}$ hours.

What was needed was a much better engine to make the wheel turn, and a much smoother, more reliable road-bed for it to turn on. For all the rigid horse collars and lever brakes and elliptical springs amounted to no more than dabbling in technological alternatives when the real need was for an entirely new system of transportation. Happily, in England and parts of the United States, a few imaginative men were experimenting with just such a system—powered by steam and running on a road of steel—to meet the demands for mobility of a society which had plunged into the Industrial Revolution.

The Great
Invention

The wheel must be ranked as man's greatest technical triumph. There was nothing like it in nature to copy or adapt; it had to be created whole in a giant leap of the human imagination. When it was finally achieved, by some unknown genius in Sumer more than 5,000 years ago, it decisively and permanently altered the course of civilization. The wheel's influence on society has been so great that the history of nations can be written in terms of the development of their wheeled transportation. With carts, ancient farmers could transport their surplus crops to the growing cities so that other men were free to turn to non-agricultural pursuits. The war chariots of Assyria and Egypt helped to make their armies —and kingdoms—the mightiest of their time. The prairie schooner and the stage-coach led America's dynamic westward movement.

Today the wheels of yester-year continue to roll slowly in many remote corners of the world; wherever this is so, they serve as indicators of stunted technology and culture. The wooden-spoked wheels of the humble gypsy wagon opposite are such living relics of an era when the creak and crunch of millions of animal-drawn vehicles marked the travels of mankind.

THE LAST WORD IN WAGONS
A contemporary Spanish gypsy wagon embodies virtually all the achievements of the wagon maker's ancient craft. The ironclad rear wheels, almost five feet in diameter, roll easily over poor roads, while the smaller front wheels pivot under the body for manœuvrability. The rear-wheel brake and metal body springs were among the last refinements.

A World without Wheels

Before there were any wheels, men moved heavy loads by dragging. The first land vehicles may have been hollowed-out tree trunks used by Stone Age hunters to haul animal carcasses to their camp sites. By 5000 B.C., these crude land carriers had been developed into sledges—platforms on runners—like the ones the Egyptians employed (*below*) to haul huge monuments and the massive limestone blocks from which the great pyramids at Giza were fashioned.

When the time came to improve on the sledge, the wheel was probably used immediately without any intermediate stage, such as fixed rollers. But the change from sledge to wagon was neither complete nor universal. The Eyptians used sledges long after the wheel had been introduced into the Nile Valley, because sledges slid easily over sandy soil where wheels tended to sink. In Lapland, sledges like that on the right have been used since around 5000 B.C. to drag goods over slippery grass and marsh in the summer, snow and ice in the winter.

In the Western Hemisphere, Indians continued to use the sledge-like travoise—a V-shaped cargo carrier consisting of two wooden shafts dragged by a dog—after the Europeans had brought wagons on to the American plains. Even when the tribesmen were confronted with that other European innovation, the horse, they still declined to put wheels on the ends of the shafts; instead they simply used the horse to replace the dog.

LAPLAND'S AGELESS SLEDGE

A horse-drawn sledge, being used to harvest hay during the brief summer in Swedish Lapland, is remarkably similar to prehistoric sledges excavated from near-by bogs. During the severe Lapland winters, the sledge is virtually the only means of over-land transportation in the region.

THE STATUE-MOVERS OF EGYPT

Sledging a sacred statue from its temple was a common festival ritual in ancient Egypt. The wall painting below shows priests hauling forth the statue of deified Queen Ahmose Nofret-iry around 1300 B.C. The boat-like pieces and kiosk enclosure are part of the statue's setting.

AN UNCHANGING DESIGN
The bullock-carts shown on these pages are almost identical, but they are separated in time by 4,000 years. The one on this page is still used on the primitive farms of Turkish Anatolia; the other is a clay model of a vehicle used by the Harappa civilization of the Indus Valley in 2000 B.C. The only notable improvement in the contemporary cart is its protective metal tyres.

The Wooden Wheels of Sumer

No one knows why the Sumerians, who invented the wheel, chose to assemble it from three wooden planks instead of cutting a slice off a round log. Some archaeologists believe that large trees were scarce in Mesopotamia; others theorize that the Sumerians found that a one-piece wheel would soon split along the grain. Whatever the reason, the wheel they devised was solid but composite— two rounded planks braced to either side of a centre plank which was pierced to accommodate the end of a one-piece wooden axle.

The Sumerian invention may first have been used on wagons that were actually convertible sledges, with four wheels and a pair of axles which could be quickly removed for crossing rough terrain or fording streams. Motive power was probably supplied

by a pair of yoked oxen pulling on either side of a single shaft.

The earliest crude wagons were soon followed by two-wheeled chariots drawn by teams of asses, and also by two-wheeled ox-carts, like those shown above. Such vehicles probably introduced the solid wheel to Assyria around 3000 B.C., and to the steppes of central Asia and the Indus Valley shortly after 2500 B.C.

Where the wheel went, roads appeared—though at first they were often merely well-worn ruts connecting neighbouring settlements—and wheeled migrations began. One of the earliest of these treks was recorded by the Egyptians, whose drawings show the solid-wheeled ox-carts that carried a horde of migrants some 500 miles from their Anatolian homeland to the borders of Egypt in 1194 B.C.

A Legacy from a Chariot Wheel

Around 2000 B.C. a completely new wheel, tailored for the speed of the horse rather than the strength of the ox, appeared. Spoked instead of solid, this new wheel first rolled over the ancient world on the swift, highly manœuvrable war chariots with which the invading Indo-European tribes overwhelmed the older civilizations of Egypt and the Near East.

The spoked wheel was harder to construct, but lighter and more efficient than the solid wheel. At the centre of its design was a separate wooden hub hollowed to fit over an axle tip. Holes bored into the hub held four to eight wooden spokes, connecting the hub to a circular wooden rim, or felloe, that consisted of as many as six joined sections of heat-bent wood.

Refinements of the spoked wheel were soon forthcoming. Assyrian war chariots (*right*) were among the first to boast metal tyres, copper or bronze strips that were set on to the rim to increase the wheel's durability. In Egypt skilled wheelwrights employed such sophisticated techniques as lamination and mortising to join thin wooden pieces into extremely light but sturdy wheels. And the Celts of Central Europe learned to form an excellent rim by bending a single length of wood into a complete circle.

Over the years many varieties of wheeled vehicles were developed— but the spoked wheel itself was not superseded until the 19th century.

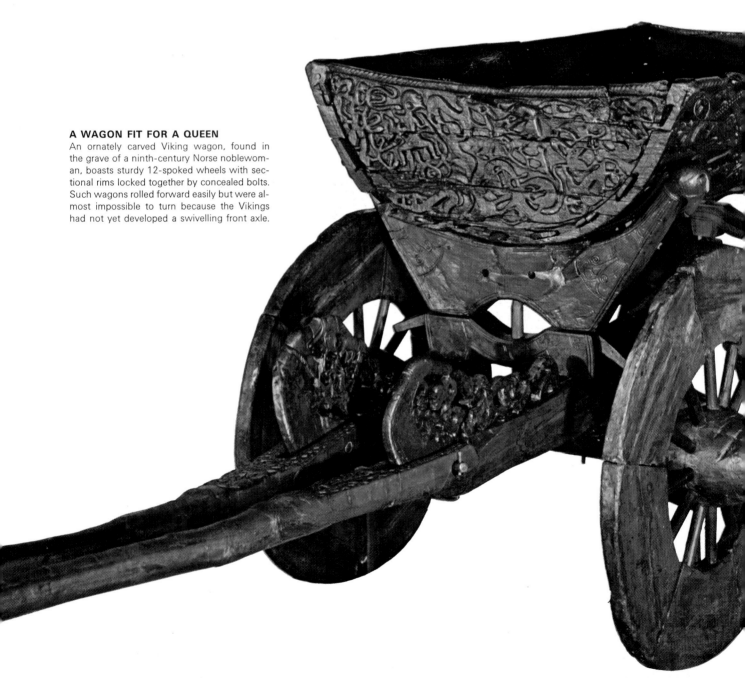

A WAGON FIT FOR A QUEEN
An ornately carved Viking wagon, found in the grave of a ninth-century Norse noblewoman, boasts sturdy 12-spoked wheels with sectional rims locked together by concealed bolts. Such wagons rolled forward easily but were almost impossible to turn because the Vikings had not yet developed a swivelling front axle.

The chariot was used in Assyria not only for war but for sport. This ninth-century B.C. relief shows King Assurnasirpal II hunting lions.

SYMBOLS OF A LIVING PAST

The bullock and the cartwheel still supply the basic transportation of India, where 10 million carts, little advanced in more than 3,000 years, continue in use. The wheel, remarkably similar to the Viking model on the left, has a rim of six wooden sections connected to the hub by three sets of spokes. The metal tyre and the long wooden fender, which protects the wheel from collision damage, are centuries-old improvements. The cart is pulled along slowly by a pair of yoked bullocks, controlled by the ancient device of lines running through their noses.

Wagons for the Long Haul

It was the road-building Romans who first realized the potential of horse-drawn wheels in commerce and overland transportation. Rome's first vehicles were derived from primitive Greek models. But by the first century B.C. Roman wainwrights had discovered the superb Celtic wagons of Western Europe and had adopted innovations: swivelling front axles for steerability, one-piece rims and tyres to add strength, and metal-lined hubs to reduce friction.

By A.D. 200 sturdy Roman wagons were clattering over 50,000 miles of main roads. Mail and passenger vehicles like the one on the left could cover 100 miles in 24 hours, with frequent stops to change horses. The teams tired quickly because the Roman improvements in wagons were not matched by developments in harness design. Breast- and bellybands, painful and power-wasting, were still used to hitch the horses to a centre pole. Not until the 12th century did the efficient padded horse collar and parallel shafts come into general use.

Well before that time, however—perhaps as early as 400 B.C.—a remarkably utilitarian vehicle (*below*) had begun to evolve on the Russian steppes. It could be used as an open farm wagon or converted for overland travel by enclosing the body with a cloth canopy drawn over high-arched hoops. This conveyance, still used in many parts of Eastern Europe, may be an ancestor of the familiar prairie schooner of 19th-century America.

DELIVERING THE ROMAN MAIL
A Roman wagon, depicted on a relief set into a church wall at Klagenfurt, Austria, may have carried mail when the city was the Roman settlement of Virunum. The relief formerly adorned the tomb believed to be that of Ulbius Gajanus, a fifth-century postmaster of Virunum.

A TURKISH COVERED WAGON
Resembling a vision of America's Old West, a springless covered wagon moves along a dirt road in Turkey. Like its larger American counterpart, it has small front wheels for easy turning, a removable canvas top, and flareboards, or wings, to expand cargo space above the wheels.

A Cart for East and West

With the fall of the Roman Empire and its fragmentation into warring feudal domains, the development of wheeled vehicles in Europe actually regressed. Rome's roads succumbed to centuries of neglect in the Middle Ages. During this period the most practical vehicle was the two-wheeled cart, which could travel over rough terrain.

In China, this same type of cart had furnished basic transportation for centuries. The Chinese had never developed roads good enough for four-wheeled wagons. Not until around 200 B.C. did an attempt begin to replace the ancient cart paths radiating from the inland capital of Ch'ang-an with gravel-topped roads. By the seventh-century, when China under the T'ang emperors had become the world's busiest trade centre, merchant carts like the one on the left came from as far west as Persia, carrying goods to exchange for China's silks and spices. The Chinese two-wheeled cart was introduced into feudal Japan at about this time; it is a tribute to its design that a thousand years later (*below, right*) it had still undergone little change.

By then, Europe was rapidly recovering from the Middle Ages and new vehicles were beginning to appear. In France, thrifty peasants had adapted their carts to the powerful horses originally bred to carry medieval knights; one result was the *tombereau*, or tipcart (*right*), still being used on thousands of French farms.

THE WHEELS OF CHINA
A merchant's cart, reproduced in this ceramic group, has high, multispoked wheels typical of seventh-century China. But this type of bullock was uncommon in China, and the features of the owner (*right*) appear foreign, indicating that the cart may have been that of a nomadic trader.

THE WHEELS OF JAPAN
Drawn by a bullock and 19 straining men, aided by others pushing and prying from behind, a huge cart carries a draped load of stone in this 17th-century Japanese painting. Freeloading singers on top of the cart urge the men on, while lounging samurai observe from the sidelines.

In 20th-century France a farmer's tipcart, its hinged bed unlatched to dump a load of fertilizer, shares a field with a modern tractor.

The Golden Age of Coaching

In its brief but dashing career, the horse-drawn coach reigned as king of the road. Specifically designed to accommodate passengers, the coach at first was little more than a windowed box suspended by leather straps over a springless chassis. Passengers in the two facing seats had to endure constant swaying and bouncing. Public stage-coaches set off a boom in overland travel beginning in the 17th century and elaborate private coaches became royal status symbols. One of the most lavishly ornate of these was the gold-encrusted State Coach (*right*). Constructed for King George III of England in 1763, it was called "the most superb carriage ever built".

Although the coach was improved over the years by such additions as springs, brakes and even rubber tyres, there was no way to make a team of horses run faster. Then came the railways. The stage-coach fought a losing battle with the steam-powered train until 1904, when the last noteworthy stage-coach run in the United States—between the Nevada bonanza towns of Tonopah and Goldfield—was ended.

A CARRIAGE FOR CORONATIONS
A gilded symbol of British grandeur, the seldom-used State Coach, seen here from the rear, requires eight horses to move its four-ton weight. Improvements have been added to ease the undulating ride in its leather-slung body, but the 18th-century coach is still notorious among members of the royal family for its lack of comfort.

2

The Arrival
of Steam

The chaos that engine-driven wheels could
bring was already a concern in 1842, when
this cartoon satirized the disastrous conse-
quences to be expected from the further
development of steam-propelled carriages.

IN THE EARLY YEARS of the 19th century, Oliver Evans, an American steam-engine builder with an uncanny eye for the future, made a prediction: "The time will come when people will travel by steam-engines, from one city to another, almost as fast as birds fly. A carriage will set out from Washington in the morning, the passengers will breakfast at Baltimore, dine in Philadelphia, and sup in New York the same day".

Wild as his prophecy sounded at the time, the truth was that by the year 1800 all the technology for a steam-powered railway was already in hand, waiting for the right man to put it together. The rails and wheels were certainly there; even before 1600, flange-wheeled carts pulled by horses were running over wooden tramways in the mines of Europe. By 1760, Abraham Darby, owner of a thriving English iron foundry, had improved this part of the technology to an astonishing degree. "He got roads made with sleepers and rails", wrote his wife Abiah proudly. "One waggon with three horses will bring as much as twenty [pack] horses used to. Of late years the laying of rails of cast Iron was substituted. . . . We have in the different Works near twenty miles of this road. Iron Wheels . . . for these waggons was I believe my Husband's Invention."

More important, steam power had been harnessed, and with a few crucial refinements would soon be ready to move a train of loaded wagons. By 1800, in Great Britain alone 496 steam-powered piston engines were pumping out flooded mines and providing a cheap, reliable source of power for foundries and factories. According to the calculations of one British industrial baron of the time, whose factory at Soho was the very model of a modern manufactory, a single bushel of coal (94 pounds) poured into the hopper of a steam-engine would produce the same amount of work in one hour as 10 horses. To supply this new source of power, British coal production rose from 4,750,000 to 10 million tons between 1750 and 1800. Imports of raw cotton for steam-powered mills went from 3 million to 56 million pounds. By 1800, pig-iron production had soared to 250,000 tons. The Industrial Revolution had arrived. Now there was an urgent need to find new ways to haul raw materials to the factories, and then to carry finished goods to new markets.

James Watt, whose invention of the separate condenser in 1765 had made the steam-engine a more practical tool for industry, toyed with "the application of the steam-engine . . . to driving wheel carriages". However, his engines had some severe limitations. The earliest ones worked by the force of the atmosphere thrusting on a piston, after condensation of steam had created a vacuum in the cylinder. But even in Watt's later engines, the pressure never went much higher than about 15 pounds per square inch. And while these machines were good enough to power a cotton loom or to run a mine pump, they were much too large and clumsy to propel a land vehicle.

The right engine made its appearance on a steam wagon built in 1769 by Nicolas Cugnot, a French Army engineer. Unlike Watt's engine, Cugnot's worked by the direct force of high-pressure steam against each of two pistons. The wagon itself, driven by a system of ratchets and pawls, managed to make a few runs, showing very poor speed—about two m.p.h.—but excellent potential. The French government had other things on its mind, so Cugnot and his marvellous machine died in obscurity.

This quiet little drama, barely recorded by history, was nevertheless the most important event in land transportation since the invention of the wheel itself. For the first time a wheel could travel in any direction powered by something other than human or animal muscle. Furthermore, the basic function of the wheel was completely altered. Until then the wheel of a wagon had been simply a passive device for reducing the friction between the load and the surface of the ground. But when Cugnot geared up his engine to transmit power to the wheels themselves, those wheels became levers which actually drove the load. This is the basic principle by which all railway trains and motor-cars and lorries run today. But the unfortunate M. Cugnot was the wrong man in the wrong place at the wrong time.

In America, Oliver Evans, the prophet of the steam railway, fared only a little better. Evans designed several excellent high-pressure engines and offered them to various wagon builders and turnpike companies; but, complained Evans, he never "found a person willing to contribute to the expense or even encourage me". However, Evans did win a contract from the Philadelphia Board of Health for a steam-powered dredging scow. To make it move, he built a new kind of engine nicknamed a grasshopper because of the peculiar action of its piston rod, which was connected to the wheels through a series of horizontal and vertical beams: when the engine operated, the rod and beams moved up and down like the hind legs of a grasshopper. To prove the motive power of steam, he decided to run the whole contraption under its own power through the streets of the city.

The prophet's lament

As Evans described it, the machine proceeded "with a gentle motion up Market-street and around the Centre Square, and we concluded from the experiment that the engine was able to rise any ascent allowed by law on turnpike roads, which is not more than four degrees".

Still nobody cared. Thoroughly disgusted, Evans went back to designing industrial engines.

Meanwhile, here in England there was another, even more inventive man whom the world was treating just as badly. He was an impetuous, broad-shouldered Cornishman named Richard Trevithick, "a man of great powers of mind but [who] would often run wild from want of calculations". In 1801, Trevithick completed his first steam-powered road carriage, which he tested over Christmas week. On the 28th December, with a cluster of friends, Trevithick took off in the machine, went up a hill,

A HORSELESS GUN CARRIAGE like the one below, designed for the French Army by Nicolas Cugnot, was one of the world's first full-sized steam-propelled vehicles. Steam from a forward boiler passed through a curved pipe into a pair of cylinders, forcing down the piston rods that turned the single front wheel. The vehicle barely topped two miles an hour, and was limited to 15-minute runs by its boiler capacity. Since the driving wheel was set in a fixed position, turns were negotiated by swivelling the entire front end of the vehicle.

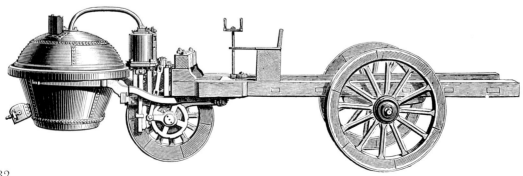

then broke down. "The carriage was forced under some shelter," reported one witness, "and the parties adjourned to the hotel, and comforted their hearts with a roast goose, and proper drinks, when, forgetful of the engine, its water boiled away, the iron became red hot, and nothing that was combustible remained, either of the engine or the house."

Trevithick promptly built another steam carriage, embodying several developments which would later be used in commercial locomotives. The furnace was set inside the boiler, so that the hot vapours could help to heat the water before passing out into the chimney. Even more important, however, was the dynamic principle of double action by high-pressure steam, which pushed the piston both forward and back, eliminating the vacuum that had been the prime power source in most earlier engines. In an early trial in London, the machine got up to eight m.p.h. Some time after this triumph, Trevithick packed up for Pen-y-darran in Wales, where Samuel Homfray, owner of an iron mill, bet a neighbour 500 guineas that a steam wagon could run with a load of cars over the cast-iron tramway tying his foundry to the Glamorganshire Canal. To help in winning the bet, Trevithick assembled all the best ideas he could pluck from his own mind and from the scrap heaps of Evans's and Cugnot's failures.

On the 22nd February 1804, Trevithick reported, "Yesterday we proceeded on our journey with the engine; we carried 10 tons of iron, five waggons, and seventy men riding on them the whole journey. . . . The gentleman that bet 500 guineas against it rode the whole journey with us, and is satisfied that he has lost the bet".

The Cornishman's legacy

Four years later, Trevithick pulled a coachful of customers behind a locomotive at an exhibition in London. This was the world's first passenger train—just as the Pen-y-darran tram had been the first freight, and the London carriage the first good horseless wagon. "I thought", wrote Trevithick, "[these experiments] would show to the public quite enough to recommend its general use: but though promising to be of so much consequence, has so far remained buried, which discourages me from trying its practice." Trevithick was more than discouraged. After 25 years of chasing other dreams, he died, so poor that friends had to take up a collection to buy his coffin.

The world owed Dick Trevithick a good deal more. Thanks to him, the technology to build a steam railway was all in one piece. Furthermore, as one historian put it, "England was socially and economically ripe for the railroad". Very soon, other engineers and businessmen, by providing equal parts of technological refinement and lusty promotion, were about to bring up Trevithick's child—and prosper from its labours.

Trevithick's engine, with its thumping, pounding single piston, quickly gave way to engines with pairs of alternating pistons. One of the most imaginative of the locomotive builders was William Chapman, an English engineer, who also foresaw the modern passenger and dining coaches—"long carriages resting on eight wheels and containing the means of providing the passengers with breakfast, dinner, etc., whilst the carriages are moving". A colliery supervisor, William Hedley, and his chief mechanic, Timothy Hackworth, built an engine with the cylinders down close to the driving wheels, where cylinders, in essence, would remain throughout the subsequent history of the steam locomotive. With this accomplishment Hedley declared himself the "Father of the Locomotive Engine". Of course he was not; and neither was any other man.

But while Hedley was huffing and puffing, there laboured in a nearby colliery a wiry, hot-headed North Country man who would one day be able to lay as honest a claim to the title as any man. George Stephenson was born close to a minehead at Wylam in Northumberland. While still a small boy, he had a regular job at the mine, first as a coal sorter, later as horse driver at the pit-head. Stephenson had a native genius with machines, and soaked up their workings through his pores as he grew up, repairing and improving the hoist engines and pumps at the mines. By 1812 he was an enginewright at Killingworth. By 1813, he was practising as a civil engineer with a reputation as the most knowledgeable hand with a steam-engine in the Northumbrian district. True to that reputation, in July 1814 he completed a five-ton steam locomotive called the *Blucher*, which hauled a load of eight wagons, weighing about 30 tons, over the tramway of the Killingworth colliery.

During the next decade, Stephenson built perhaps a dozen more like the *Blucher*. And though the design was more of the order of an improvement than a breakthrough, the self-assured Stephenson observed, "I am confident a railway on which my engines can work is far superior to a *canal*. On a long and favourable railway I would [wager] my engines [could] travel 60 miles per day with from 40 to 60 tons of goods".

The challenge

Indeed he would. But first it was necessary to get the public thinking and caring about locomotives. Until now all the existing steam railway lines—and every one of the dozen or so locomotives running on them—were private affairs, operated in collieries and ironworks, where the best engines had already proved themselves more economical than horses (about 70 per cent of the cost per ton-mile) for hauling freight. What the locomotive needed now was a public showcase.

To provide one and perhaps make some money into the bargain, a group of promoters—with whom George Stephenson signed on as engineer—got busy selling Parliament on a public railway line between the coal town of Darlington and the port of Stockton. The engine George Stephenson produced for the inaugural run was a stout, reliable grasshopper type. Its one improvement was a pair of connecting rods linking the front and rear wheels, a device which ensured that the

A PIONEER LOCOMOTIVE, designed by Richard Trevithick, builder of the first railway engine, was powered by high-pressure steam. The steam actuated a piston that pushed the slanting connecting rod (*at centre*) to and fro to turn the geared wheels. The momentum of the large flywheel (*right*), which was attached to the piston through a connecting rod on the other side, kept the piston moving.

wheels would all rotate at the same speed as the machine moved forward.

On the 27th September 1825, the engine, christened *Locomotion*, hooked into a line of wagons in which were packed some 600 thrilled and slightly nervous passengers. With a roar of steam and a clank of chain couplings, the train got under way, as the passengers cheered and stage-coach drivers on near-by roads urged their horses along to keep up with the engine. At 3.45 p.m., three hours after it had started from Darlington 12 miles away, the world's first public railway train pulled into Stockton Quay to the thundering approval of 40,000 onlookers, the ear-splitting salutes of seven 18-pound cannons, the ringing of church bells, and a rousing rendition of *God Save the King* from a whole phalanx of brass bands.

That night everyone, including George Stephenson, got roaring drunk. "The man who can now *hesitate* to recommend steam-engines instead of horsepower", crowed a contemporary, "must be pitied for his ignorance or despised for his obstinacy."

"Railways must today be reckoned as the chief means of speedy and cheap transport", wrote another. "Storm, snow, and dust have no effect on it. . . . Canals lag behind by 5 m.p.h.; moreover the cost is 5 to 1."

These words were all true. But they were uttered mainly by Stephenson's friends. Both Stephenson and the steam locomotive still had plenty of enemies. The canal people had powerful lobbies in Parliament, and strong-arm gangs in the field, where more than one railway bridge or freshly laid stretch of track was mysteriously torn up on a dark night. One canal company went as far as to turn a bombardment of gunfire on a survey gang of Stephenson's. From other quarters, there was a bombardment of invective and scepticism by critics who either doubted the prowess of the steam locomotive, or who were simply partial to the horseflesh which had served so long and faithfully.

The rebuttal

"What can be more palpably absurd and ridiculous", demanded the *Quarterly Review* of March 1825, "than the prospect held out of locomotives travelling twice as fast as stage coaches! We should as soon expect the people . . . to suffer themselves to be fired off upon one of Congreve's ricochet rockets as to trust themselves to the mercy of such a machine going at such a rate."

Even among the supporters of the steam-engine, there was a notion that its true place was on the common road, where Trevithick had first put it with his London carriage, rather than on rails.

Roused to new action by such words, George Stephenson joined another syndicate, whose purpose was to build a railway between Liverpool and Manchester. On this railway, the elder Stephenson and his brilliant son Robert would prove that the steam locomotive was the best medicine for Great Britain, and furthermore that steam belonged on rails. The proof was dramatic, established in a competition that the board of the Liverpool and Manchester line held "on the level space between the two inclined planes at Rainhill" to determine the best kind

ROCKET

NOVELTY

SANS PAREIL

THREE EARLY LOCOMOTIVES that competed in a series of tests at Rainhill, England, in 1829 gave final proof that steam could be used to power railway lines. The *Sans Pareil*, a bulky engine that chugged noisily along the track and puffed great billows of smoke, was eliminated from the tests when one part after another failed. The *Novelty*, a light, beautifully designed engine, suffered a series of mishaps and was finally withdrawn by its inventors when its boiler tube sprang a leak. The only engine to survive the gruelling trial was the *Rocket*, which had inclined cylinders and a multitubular boiler, shown in detail on the opposite page.

of mechanical wagon. In the trial, each machine was to make 20 runs to and fro over a one-and-a-half-mile course hauling a load of stone-filled wagons three times the engine's weight. The winning locomotive would receive the blessing of the Liverpool and Manchester, and the designer would receive a prize of £500.

On the 6th October 1829, the opening day of the trials, 10,000 stout English folk turned out to witness an event which would, as the Liverpool newspaper of that day predicted, "alter the whole system of our internal communications . . . substituting an agency whose ultimate effects can scarcely be anticipated". Five entries showed up, the thin cream of the 19th century's first major crop of self-propelled land wagons. Of these, one was an hilarious contraption powered by two horses on a treadmill, which clattered charmingly past the flag-draped stands a number of times, more a diversion than a serious entry. Another, gravely wounded when the freight wagon bearing it to the trials tipped over, staggered through a gallant exhibition run, then withdrew. That left three serious competitors to be judged: an adaptation of the steam road carriage called the *Novelty*; a vertical-cylinder powerhouse of a locomotive named *Sans Pareil* built by Timothy Hackworth, an engine designer whom many considered to be the equal of the Stephensons; and a new creation called the *Rocket*, designed primarily by Robert Stephenson, under the canny eye of his father and a hard-driving colleague named Henry Booth.

The crowd's favourite, noted one observer, was the *Novelty*, whose "great lightness [and] beautiful workmanship . . . excited universal admiration". "Almost at once," said the witness, "*Novelty* darted off at the amazing velocity of 28 miles an hour, and it actually did one mile in the incredibly short space of one minute and 53 seconds." But when *Novelty* hooked on a heavy load for a subsequent run, there was a loud boom accompanied by a roiling of smoke, sparks and flame. The furnace had blown back. Mercifully no one was hurt, but after two more mishaps the *Novelty* was, for all practical purposes, out of the running.

Run for the money

The crowd turned to Stephenson's *Rocket*. Not handsome to the eye, it nevertheless contained two crucial design features which were to make it the prototype for steam locomotives over the next century. Instead of using a complicated system of cranks and gears, *Rocket*'s piston rods were connected directly to driving pins on the front wheels. And what is more, its horizontal boiler, though covered with what looked like the shell of an old-fashioned, one-piece hollow boiler, was actually an extensive network of 25 three-inch copper tubes conducting the whirling hot gases from the engine's fire. These gases then heated the water and converted it to steam far more quickly and efficiently than had been possible in the old boilers.

On the first few runs Stephenson, with his son Robert riding the engine beside him, held the *Rocket* to a conservative top speed of about $14\frac{1}{2}$ m.p.h. By the 10th run he had nudged it up to about 21. On the final lap, with the taste of victory in his mouth, George Stephenson opened the *Rocket* to full power. The engine leaped forward and boomed across the finish line at 29 m.p.h. while 10,000 cheered and the judges looked with astonishment at their watches.

"George S. or Robert S. has come off triumphant and of course will take hold of the £500 so liberally offered by the Company", reported an eyewitness, after Hackworth's *Sans Pareil* suffered an anticlimactic breakdown. "None of the others were able to come near. . . . . The *Rocket* is by far the best Engine I have ever seen for Blood and Bone united."

Run for the lady

As a final flourish to his victory, the lusty old North Country man began gunning the *Rocket* up and down the line, giving rides to anyone bold enough to dare the new dimension in speed. In the months that followed, a fair number of adventuresome souls rode the iron rails of the new Liverpool and Manchester road. One thoroughly dazzled passenger was the lovely young actress Fanny Kemble, who rode alongside Stephenson on the locomotive. "The engine was set off at its utmost speed, swifter than a bird flies", she bubbled after the journey. "You cannot conceive what that sensation of cutting the air was; the motion as smooth as possible too. . . . I stood up, and with my bonnet off 'drank the air before me'. . . . The wind absolutely weighed my eyelids down. . . . When I closed my eyes this sensation of flying was quite delightful and strange beyond description; yet strange as it was, I had a perfect sense of security and not the slightest fear." With that, Fanny reported, she fell quite in love with Mr. Stephenson and his wonderful engine.

So did most of the rest of the world. And when, three weeks later, the Stephensons delivered the *Planet*, with a boiler containing 129 tubes, it proved so fast, economical and reliable that no sensible man could continue to debate the merits of the steam railway. Overland transport was no longer limited to the speed of a galloping horse or to the strength of a group of animals in harness. Rain and mud were no hazards. The time for talk, for fighting and for fumbling experiments was over. On the Liverpool and Manchester line the cost of hauling coal dropped to two pence per ton-mile—compared to the ruinous old road-wagon rate of ten pence. By 1833, virtually every lump of commercial coal dug in England made some part of its trip to market in a railway car. And by 1836 more than 450 miles of rails tied together the major industries of the United Kingdom—mainly because of "the genius of Mr. Stephenson and his son".

In America, too, by 1836 the astonishing total of 1,273 miles of track reached out across the U.S. from Boston to Savannah, from New York to Central Ohio. That year the Mohawk and Hudson and the B&O each carried over 100,000 passengers. "Steam is annihilating distance!" became the rallying cry of the backers of the iron horse. And in about 30 more years, in 1867 to be exact, a railway train set out from Washington in the morning, and the passengers supped in New York the same day, just as Oliver Evans had always known they would.

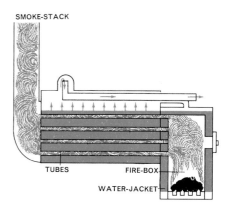

SMOKE-STACK

TUBES　　　　　FIRE-BOX

WATER-JACKET

A TRIUMPHANT DESIGN, the boiler of the successful locomotive *Rocket* contained the secret of its good performance. The best previous boilers had one or two tubes to convey hot gases from the fire and thus convert water into steam; the *Rocket* had 25. By increasing the area of the water-heating surface, the multiple tubes greatly augmented the *Rocket's* steam production and reduced its fuel consumption by about 40 per cent.

An Iron Horse
on Tracks of Steel

In the early part of the 19th century, a wave of unfamiliar sounds broke over the hitherto peaceful English countryside —the rumbling of iron wheels on iron rails, the clank of car couplings, the rhythmic chuff of steam as it pulsed through the loins of a powerful new creature called the locomotive. In the years that followed, the distinctive din of the railway spread around the world, heralding perhaps the most fascinating race of machines the world has ever seen. Locomotives ranged in size, shape and utility from the rattling, eight-ton pioneers of the early 1800's—such as the *Stourbridge Lion* (*right*), a British-made engine that introduced rail travel to America—to the 700,000-pound machines which ultimately pulled 100-coach goods trains over the passes of the high Rockies. These engines, with their booming heartbeat and their mournful cry, changed the transportation habits of the world. Not only could the locomotive carry up to 13,000 tons to the horse wagon's four, but on rails the loads moved 15 times as fast and at one-tenth the cost. By the turn of the century virtually all inter-city passengers and freight in the U.S. moved by train, and there was scarcely a village in the land which had not heard the hoof-beat of the iron horse.

PIONEER OF THE NEW BREED
The first railway engine to run in the U.S., the *Stourbridge Lion* managed a modest 10 m.p.h. in a trial near Honesdale, Pennsylvania, on the 8th August 1829. Like many of the earliest engines, this one was of the so-called grasshopper type, a name derived from the peculiar action of the vertical piston rods and horizontal wooden beam on top of the boiler.

The Promise of a New Prosperity

By 1832 England boasted two dozen commercial railways, the most prosperous carrying 350,000 people and 70,000 tons of cargo a year. Most of the machines that hauled the traffic in the new way were built by the masterful engineering team of George and Robert Stephenson. Mainly, they were of the *Rocket* type (*centre*) or the later *Planet* (*top and bottom*). These were the Stephensons's two most far-sighted creations, having high-pressure boilers with intricate networks of internal piping and pairs of horizontal cylinders which set the general pattern for future steam locomotives. Though they weighed no more than eight tons, these sturdy engines pulled strings of up to a dozen loaded passenger or freight cars at the remarkable average speed for the period of 21 m.p.h.

The most popular of the early railways was the Liverpool and Manchester, shown below: in the last four months of 1830 it carried 70,000 pas-

A first-class train (*top*) on the Liverpool and Manchester line carried passengers in comfort with plush seats and glazed windows. But second-

sengers, and the following year it grossed half a million pounds, transporting everything from a "swinish multitude [to] a multitude of swine", according to one waspish contemporary. Unfortunately, the rudimentary technology of the era made schedules so uncertain that neither the multitude nor the swine could know when —or if—they would arrive at the end of the 30-mile line. Though the trains departed on a fixed time-table, the chief chronicler of the L&M admitted that the railway's owners "appear to have considered it more prudent not to tie themselves down to any times of arrival, which are not indicated". When these early trains did arrive, they did not always stop where they were supposed to, because most of them managed without such frills as brakes. The engineer just coasted the locomotive, and then gave a loud toot on a tin carriage horn—where upon the male passengers leaped out and helped to wrestle the train to a halt.

class (*centre*) and livestock (*bottom*) trains hauled their loads in the open, "exposed to . . . the steam, and in the winter . . . [the] cold".

America
Begins to Move

The success of the English railways set off a flurry of invention by American engineers. Before the Liverpool and Manchester had finished its first fat fiscal year, U.S. engine works had built half a dozen new locomotives. One, the 10-horsepower *DeWitt Clinton* (*left*), ran for almost a year between Albany and Schenectady before it was peacefully retired.

Some of those early runs were marvels of chaos and confusion. Sparks from the stack rained down on the travellers. Umbrellas raised as shields went up in flames; and part of each trip was usually spent thumping a neighbour's back to put out the fire on his smouldering greatcoat.

Despite the hazards of early railway travel, the speed, capacity and smoothness of the ride proved far superior to that of the animal-drawn stage. Small boys and grown men gathered at the depot to watch the engines in wide-eyed admiration. Before very long, minstrels began to sing the glories of the great trains such as *Old 97*, and the *Wabash Cannonball*. And the friendly man at the throttle, with his visored hat and his striped denims, became the beau ideal in a century-long love affair between America at large and the steam locomotive.

THE PATTERN OF POWER
The *DeWitt Clinton*, shown in this oil painting leaving the station for the first time, got her power from two pistons which thrust against a cranked axle connected to the forward wheels. To move those pistons, steam from the boiler collected in the tall dome behind the smokestack, and then travelled down to the cylinders.

Fruit of a Friendly Struggle

During the 1830's and early 1840's, a lusty rivalry grew up between British and American railwaymen for leadership in laying rails and building locomotives. Britain had a head start, but in the year 1832 alone, some 17 brand-new steam railways were chartered in the U.S., and soon more than half a dozen locomotive works sprang up along the East Coast. The engines built in these works were so good that within a few years U.S. firms were doing a lively export business to English railways. Rising to this challenge, old-country firms began turning out heavier, stronger engines to haul their nation's commerce.

In this atmosphere the technology of the steam railway took on a new sophistication. The boiler pressures swiftly rose from 40 or 50 pounds per square inch to 120 pounds, providing proportionally more pulling power. The rigid little four-wheelers gave way to fast, flexible machines with as many as 10 wheels to provide more

THE BLESSING OF THE BOGIE
The early railway engines were stubby affairs with only two pairs of large wheels that tended to jump the track. But by 1836-1841, American engineers like William Norris and Matthias Baldwin were employing a new wheel carriage called the bogie, a swivelling forward unit of two or four small wheels which guided a locomotive smoothly around the sharpest bend.

BRITISH FOUR-WHEELER, VINTAGE 1837-1838

EARLY AMERICAN FOUR-WHEELED GOO

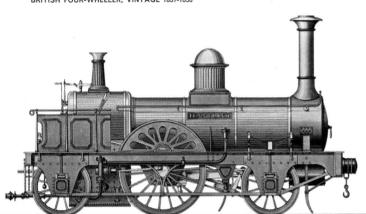

ENGLAND'S *JENNY LIND*, 1847

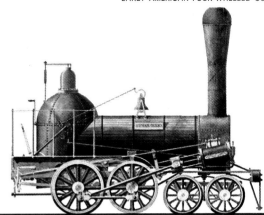

EARLY 4-4-0, BUILT BY EASTWICK & HARRISON 1839

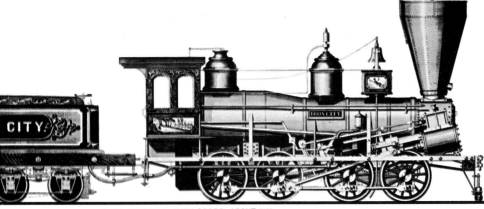

SLOW, HEAVY BALDWIN GOODS, ABOUT 1850

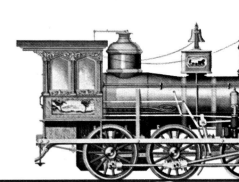

10-WHEEL GOODS AND PASSENGER ENGINE

traction for freight and greater stability for high-speed passenger trains. During this period engines on Massachusetts and New Hampshire lines got the first enclosed cabs. And in 1836, by a delightful twist of fate, one of the first steam whistles was put on a U.S. locomotive by an Army major with the appropriate name of George Whistler—better known as the husband of the lady in the world-famous painting, Whistler's "Mother".

By the mid-'40's, most of these improvements were coming from the U.S., a sprawling nation in need of the kind of overland long-distance transport which at that time only the railway could provide. And here, too, was a young nation free of the tradition that might hobble invention. "In America," said a visiting German engineer, "no one man's imprimatur is better than another's. . . . There is a rivalry here out of which grows improvement. In England it is imitation—in America it is invention."

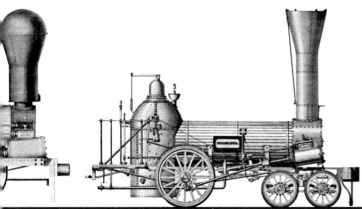

NORRIS & CO. LOCOMOTIVE WITH BOGIE, 1836

BOGIE-EQUIPPED BALDWIN GOODS ENGINE, 1841

LATER 4-4-0, WITH ENCLOSED CAB AND BRASS TRIM, 1852

BEAUTY AND BRAWN
In the 1840's England produced such dazzling machines as the pink, green and blue *Jenny Lind*. But U.S. designers had already come up with the most flexible and durable engine of all, the 4-4-0, with four wheels in the bogie and four driving wheels. Some 25,000 were built; so thoroughly did the 4-4-0 dominate U.S. railways that it was known as the American type.

THE DRIVE FOR POWER
As freight loads grew heavier, designers fashioned larger, more powerful locomotives. Baldwin produced a 30-tonner (*far left*) with no bogie and all its weight on eight drivers. A later Baldwin machine weighing 28 tons (*left*) had a four-wheel bogie ahead of six drivers. And a 10-wheel freak sometimes called a Camel (*right*) set the engineer's cab on top of the boiler.

MOUNTAIN-CLIMBING "CAMEL" GOODS LOCOMOTIVE, 1854

A New Kind of War Horse

When the American Civil War began, 30,000 miles of track crisscrossed the U.S. But fewer than 10,000 of them were in the Southern States. Worse yet for the Confederacy, its few miles of rails were situated in disconnected patches, while Union States had an integrated network of track over which they could shuttle troops, arms and supplies between points on the front.

At first this Union advantage in mobility had only a minor effect on the War, for the Confederates made superb use of what little they had, whereas some of the Union generals displayed a stubborn—and sometimes stupid—lack of appreciation of the proper function of the railway. "Be as patient as possible with the Generals", U.S. Secretary of War Stanton warned in a wire to his rail chief, Colonel Herman Haupt. "Some of them probably will trouble you more than they will the enemy."

Soon, however, the North's preponderance of rails began to tell. The Union victory at Chattanooga in November 1863 was a railway triumph: in two weeks, 23,000 men with full equipment had been switched 1,233 miles through West Virginia, Indiana and Kentucky, to arrive at the crucial hour and helped to crush the Rebels.

The South's impoverished rail lines began to disintegrate from overuse and Union raids. And though General Sherman delivered the death stroke by marching 100,000 men and 35,000 horses to Atlanta and thence to the sea, he said he could never have done it without the railways which kept supplies flowing to his troops.

A DASHING GENERAL

One of the more celebrated combatants of the Civil War was a gleaming, brass-bound locomotive named the *General*, shown above in Chattanooga's Union Station. The *General* was hijacked by Union Captain James J. Andrews and 21 cohorts, who slipped aboard the train at Marietta, Georgia, and made off with the precious machine while its passengers were having breakfast. Andrews and company managed to steam 90 miles in the stolen locomotive before three of the train's crew, using a relay of three engines, ran them down and retook the *General*.

A BATTERED PRIZE

Infantry from General U. S. Grant's Army display a ruined locomotive they seized as the Union forces broke into Richmond, Virginia. Loss of such engines—and other rail equipment—was a crippling blow to the Rebels, who had no factories to manufacture adequate replacements.

A SEASONED SOLDIER

The Federal engine *Fred Leach,* shown below just after an encounter with Confederate snipers, was typical of the workhorse 4-4-0's which helped to win the Civil War for the North. The U.S. government operated some civilian lines for war service as its own Military Railroad, running more than 400 locomotives like the *Fred Leach* over 2,000 miles of track, most of it captured in the theatres of war from the Confederates.

Monarchs of the Railway Era

Between the end of the U.S. Civil War and the turn of the century, the steam railway surged towards its dramatic climax. During that period, 160,000 miles of track were laid in the U.S., tying the East to the Far West with a dozen railway lines. And in the same decades nearly 50,000 engines were produced, filling the land with fast, heavy-duty transport.

Through mergers, interlocking directorates and freight rebates, the railways gained control of the coal, steel, cotton and wheat business. And by some old-fashioned palm-greasing, they got some of the nation's lawmakers in Washington thinking their way. Within two decades of the end of the Civil War, the rail barons had become perhaps the most powerful influence in America.

As the railways grew in power and number, so, too, did the locomotives. By the first two decades of the 20th century, American works had developed more than 100 types of engines.

MOGUL, 1875, was built to move passengers over the Allegheny Mountains. The largest locomotive of its day, the Mogul weighed 70 tons.

PRAIRIE, 1901, had 80-inch driving wheels in the model shown here, for pulling passenger trains at high speeds across the Western plains.

MALLET, 1909, was really two locomotives joined by a concealed hinge. A goods, she was named after her Swiss designer, Anatole Mallet.

48

Each of these types was tailored for a special purpose, and each had a precise wheel pattern for that purpose.

Many of these locomotives also had nicknames of their own. The 70-ton Mogul was so named (after the all-powerful Indian emperor) because of its strength: it could pull more than any other machine of its day. The Prairie's name reflected the challenge of the distances the engine was designed to cross. But perhaps the most fitting of all the names went to the goods train which the Baldwin works built for the Japanese government, designed to work effectively with the native coal of Japan. The engine's name: the Mikado. Years later, some humourless World War II bureaucrat attempted to drop the name of the enemy emperor from this machine and redesignate it as the MacArthur type, after the famous commander of the U.S. Army who directed the conquest of Japan. Happily, no one paid much attention to the bureaucrat.

CONSOLIDATION, 1883, built for use in Pennsylvania's Lehigh Valley, commemorated a merger of several lines into the Lehigh Valley Railroad.

PACIFIC, 1905, was considered by many travellers to be the best steam-engine built, with express speeds and enough power for goods.

MIKADO, 1922, built much like the Consolidation, had all the older engine's power, plus a bigger fire-box over a two-wheeled trailing truck.

49

The
Last Hurrah

The most renowned of all American steam trains was the proud and plush *Twentieth Century Limited*, a monument to railway luxury. When the first *Century* pulled out of Grand Central Station for Chicago on June 15, 1902, she carried three Pullman sleepers, a buffet and diner, a barber shop, valet, maids, stenographer and 27 coddled passengers. This was the way to travel; and when Mrs. William K. Vanderbilt, or New York's flashy Mayor Jimmy Walker, or Diamond Jim Brady went to Chicago, they rode the *Century*.

The celebrated flyer was called a *Limited* because the running time was restricted to 20 hours, a schedule of which one dazzled British journalist wrote, "Surely it is only an experiment. . . . Can so high a rate of speed . . . be maintained daily without injury to the engine?"

The *Century's* performance supplied the answer: by 1938 the time had been pared to 16 hours. But not even that running time could save the *Century* from the changing tide of technology which had swept away so much rail passenger service all over America. By the 1960's, the superior speed of the aeroplane and the lower operating costs of highway buses had made the *Century* obsolete.

THE PROUD LOOK OF POWER
Booming around the bend, a swift, 153-ton giant of the Hudson type hauls the *Century* to New York. Average speed for the 961-mile run was 60 m.p.h., with an occasional burst of as much as 85. The two flags on the top of the boiler show that another section is following.

"The Thunder of the Fast Express"

One of the last survivors of the steam age, an icicle-hung Mikado-type locomotive stands ready to begin its freight run from Montreal on a wintry day in 1960. Between 1905 and 1930 more than 14,000 of these powerful locomotives were built.

Brother, have you seen the starlight on the rails? Have you heard the thunder of the fast express? . . . the great trains cleave through gulch and gulley, they rumble with spoked thunder on the bridges over the powerful brown wash of mighty rivers, they toil through the hills, they skirt the rough brown stubble of shorn fields, they whip past empty stations in the little towns and their great stride pounds its even pulse across America.

SO WROTE THOMAS WOLFE of the era when U.S. railways had captured the commerce and the passions of the nation in a way no other instrument of man's making ever would. More than 60,000 great steel locomotives, each a masterpiece of brute power held in check by an intricate system of controls, rumbled across a webbing of track which bound together the distant corners of America. In the railways' climactic decade of 1913-1923 these engines hauled 85 per cent of the country's overland freight. One thousand million passengers annually bought tickets to travel on everything from the scurrying little electric coaches of the suburban commuter lines to the luxurious Pullman parlour cars, diners and sleepers of the *Twentieth Century Limited*. Every five seconds, a train pulled out for somewhere; and every clock in the U.S. ticked to the tempo of the railways, for Standard Time was—and is—nothing but railway time, brought in by the rail barons so that their time-tables would make sense, and later sanctified by Congress as a national convenience. There was in the land scarcely a single town which lay beyond the magic, mournful sound of a locomotive whistle. And there was scarcely a square mile of the entire nation which had not been changed by the speed and power of the railway locomotive.

In 1869 about one American in three lived in a city. West of the Missouri, the land was still so thinly settled, so forbiddingly empty that the plains and mountains were marked off on most maps as the Great American Desert. That year the first transcontinental railway went through, and large parts of the Desert bloomed into as fecund a food-producing region as any on earth. In 1884, after the spring round-ups, 825,000 head of beef cattle pushed across the Red River towards rail terminals such as Dodge City, Ogallala and Abilene, where the cowhands drank up their pay, fought, and reported back to cattle barons in letters like this: "Dear sur, we have brand 800 caves this round-up. . . . That Inglishman yu lef in charge at the other camp got to fresh and we had to kill [him]. Nothing much has hapened sence yu lef. Yurs truely, Jim".

In the very heart of the Desert during the last half of the 19th century, a wretched mining town was touched by the rails, and became a booming State Capital called Denver. New York now dined on Western beef. A San Francisco silk merchant sent his merchandise to Chicago on 50-hour delivery schedules. In Texas, Sheriff Pat Garrett shot Billy the Kid with a Colt revolver made in Hartford, Connecticut. Pittsburgh became the world's greatest steel centre and Chicago the greatest wholesale food market—and railhead—in the world. By 1920 America itself had turned into a powerful industrial nation with half its people living in cities where virtually every man, woman and child was now dependent on some distant region for food, fuel, clothing, medicine and even business.

When this astonishing metamorphosis was still in its early stages, President James A. Garfield pin-pointed the cause for an audience at Hudson College, New York: "All modern societies have entered upon a period of change more marked, more pervading, more radical than any that has occurred during the last three hundred years. . . The changes now taking place have been wrought and are being wrought, mainly, almost wholly, by a single mechanical contrivance, the steam locomotive. . . . The railway is the greatest centralizing force of modern times".

Beneath this great force for social and economic upheaval, carrying its full weight, was one tiny oval-shaped point, the size of a sixpence, where a flanged wheel rested on a steel rail. And within that tiny oval lay the secret of the low cost of transport which allowed the Birmingham, Alabama, mill-hand to spend his day making textiles for distant markets, while someone else was busy growing the beef and potatoes which the factory worker would eat when he got home at night. This secret derived from a simple yet crucial engineering characteristic: low rolling friction. On a level track, under average conditions, an engine or goods-truck wheel turned so easily on the hard, smooth rail that under ideal conditions a mere six pounds of pull could move a ton of freight. Thus, the average 500-ton freight train required only 3,000 pounds of pull to move it. Over the course of a mile, the train's engine would burn roughly 100 pounds of coal, for a fuel cost to the railway of less than five pence per mile—and a cost to the shipper of two pence per ton-mile. No more effective or inexpensive means had ever been devised for hauling goods and people overland.

The wonderful 4-4-0

By 1923, the steam locomotive which pulled these loads had evolved into more than 100 different types, each with its own colourful name and purpose. The most important single engine in this evolution was the one that railwaymen came to call the 4-4-0, using a shorthand which classifies engines by the number of wheels and the way those wheels are distributed under the engine from front to rear. The 4-4-0 had four small wheels at the front mounted on a swivelling carriage called a bogie, then four large driving wheels which received power from the pistons to drive the engine, and no wheels or trailing bogie in the rear beneath the engineer's cab. Thus the railwayman's designation, 4-4-0. To most people, however, it was simply the "American" type, for between 1840 and 1890 it dominated the railways as no other single machine ever had. Within the functional design of the 4-4-0 was all the basic technology that would be used in the most advanced locomotives of later decades.

When a designer sets out to create a locomotive, his main concern is how much pull he wants the engine to provide. This pull depends on a force called the tractive effort, which is limited by the weight of the locomotive. Under ordinary conditions no railway engine can exert more

ROUNDING A CURVE was made safer for locomotives in 1832 when a New York engineer, John B. Jervis, installed the first swivelling front bogie. As shown here in a view from above, the bogie consists of a four-wheeled platform (*black*) supporting the front of the engine on a swivel (*circle*), which permits the bogie to swing freely as it meets curves in the rails, thus guiding the locomotive around them. Soon after Jervis first introduced the front bogie, four-wheeled or two-wheeled bogies were fitted to most American engines, enabling them to maintain speed on curves without the danger of jumping the tracks.

pulling force than one-fifth the amount of weight resting on its drivers. Beyond that load, the drivers will slip on the rails. Thus a typical 4-4-0, with 50,000 pounds on its drivers, could exert a maximum of 10,000 pounds of tractive effort before its wheels began to slip. Within this limit, the tractive effort is governed by: the boiler pressure, which ultimately determines the expansive force of the steam in the cylinder; the cylinder diameter, which limits the amount of steam pushing the piston; the length of the piston stroke, which governs the maximum working period of the steam; and the diameter of the driving wheels, which act like the operating ends of levers to move the train ahead.

The other major consideration for the designer is the rate at which the pulling force is applied. This depends on the amount of steam the boiler can produce; the steam-producing capacity, in turn, is governed by the size of the fire (or the area of the grate on which the coal burns) and the total heating surface of the boiler.

"Breaking out" a long freight

Juggling with all these factors, the designers of the 4-4-0 produced in the 1860's a classic engine. Using steam at 130 pounds per square inch to force a piston in a 16-inch cylinder through a 22-inch stroke, it hauled a line of heavy goods coaches at 25 m.p.h. when equipped with 54-inch driving wheels. To get this locomotive rolling, the engineer manipulated two main controls. One was the throttle, which regulated the total amount of steam used; the other was a valve-controlling lever, or Johnson bar, which adjusted the length of time a burst of steam could push on the piston. To start, the engineer pushed the Johnson bar forward to let the steam into the cylinder for the full duration of the long, slow, powerful piston stroke needed to "break out" the line of standing cars. At the same time he opened the throttle slowly: too big a burst of steam would make the wheels spin. Once the train was rolling, he opened the throttle all the way to meet the voracious demand of the cylinders for steam; and he carefully inched back on the Johnson bar, cutting down the length of time during which the steam surged into each end of the cylinder. By balancing off the throttle and Johnson bar so that he never drew out more steam than the engine actually needed for each chuffing stroke, a good man with a feel for the pulse and pressure of his engine could save 5 to 10 per cent of his fuel over a 100-mile stretch of track.

No matter how skilful the engineer, however, the whole process of converting coal into steam-powered transportation was deplorably inefficient. The American type turned only 4 per cent of the heat-energy from its coal into pulling power. To get more work from the locomotive, designers added one or two pairs of drivers, enlarged the grate area, and supported it over a two-wheeled rear, or trailing, bogie. Not long after the turn of the century the best engines had taken on the 2-8-2 pattern of the Mikado for freight and the 4-6-2 Pacific pattern for fast passenger service. The fireman, who had had to shovel some two and a half tons of coal per hour at 133 shovelfuls to the ton, was put on easy street—

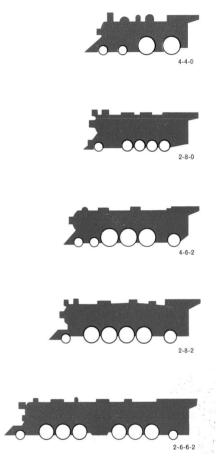

CLASSES OF LOCOMOTIVES are distinguished by the kind and number of each type's wheels. The classic 19th-century engine (*top*), for instance, is called a 4-4-0; the first digit refers to the number of wheels on the bogie at the front of the engine, the second to the number of driving wheels, and the third to the trailing bogie wheels. Large engines like the 2-6-6-2 at the bottom have an extra set of driving wheels and thus an extra digit.

some said in a feather bed—by the invention of the mechanical stoker, a screw-lift or conveyer belt from the coal tender to the fire-box. Steam pressure climbed to 200 pounds per square inch; and cylinders grew to 24 inches in diameter with a 30-inch stroke. Finally, the steam itself became more efficient through a process called superheating. On the way from boiler to cylinder, the steam was diverted back through thin pipes inside the fire-box flues, where its temperature was raised from about 175°C. to over 260°C. Because the hotter steam could expand more, it increased power output at least 20 per cent.

Breaking the 100 m.p.h. barrier

Improved in these ways, the World War I vintage locomotive got almost twice as much horsepower out of a pound of coal as did the old 4-4-0. But it still meant it converted barely 7 per cent of its heat energy into effective work, a modest performance compared to the 25 per cent efficiency of the modern diesel-electric engine. Nevertheless, it was good enough to conquer a continent. It was the means by which human beings first travelled more than 100 m.p.h., when old *999* thundered to 112.5 m.p.h. over a stretch of track outside Batavia, New York, in 1893. The man at the throttle of the formidable black machine with the gleaming steel drivers became the idol of every small boy in America. He was the Brave Engineer who dealt in cool, routine fashion with danger and death, who played with the sensitive touch of a concert violinist upon the controls of a snorting steel monster.

But while the Brave Engineer and the Iron Horse were building a nation, the owners of the railways were building an extraordinary amount of ill will through business practices which one observer described as fraught with "cunning, craft, chicane, guile and knavery". The suitably bribed North Carolina legislature once issued $6,367,000,000 in bonds to pay a ring of robber barons for building a paltry 93 miles of track worth less than one million dollars. During one 18-month period, the railways paid John D. Rockefeller something like $10 million in illegal freight rebates on his oil shipments. And in putting together his New York Central empire, old Commodore Vanderbilt once voted himself a personal bonus of $6 million in cash and $20 million in stock.

Perhaps the most glorious fraud of all occurred at Promontory, Utah, where the rails of the Union Pacific and the Central Pacific first touched to join the West Coast to the Atlantic. Each line was getting $48,000 a mile in federal loans to lay track. When they first met, instead of stopping to drive the Golden Spike, they kept right on building past each other, laying parallel track in opposite directions at $32,000 a mile until someone in Washington got wind of the hanky-panky. Then, the Golden Spike was driven, and the extra track torn up.

THE POWER OF STEAM in locomotives comes from a transfer of energy from fire to steam to mechanical motion, as shown in the drawings on these pages. Hot gases from the burning coal in the fire-box pass through a battery of narrow tubes in the waist of the locomotive to the smoke-box and escape through the smoke-stack. As the gases travel through the tubes, much of their heat is transferred to the water (*solid blue*) around the tubes. The water boils into steam (*dotted blue*), which collects in the dome and travels down the steam pipe to the cylinder. There, as shown on the opposite page, it drives the piston that turns the locomotive's wheels.

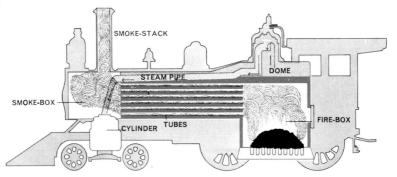

The ethical standards of railway managements before the turn of the century were matched by equally low safety standards. About 20,000 rail employees were killed or injured each year, a third of them while stepping between cars to connect the primitive link and pin couplers. Brakes were still simple, hand-powered affairs. In an emergency, when the engineer gave the signal—a shrill "brakes-down" whistle—his brakemen darted from one car to another, twisting on horizontal handwheels which slowly brought iron shoes into contact with the wheels. It was an uncertain process, and in a real pinch it could not be done fast enough.

"Every man who leaves the city by a train must cast a lingering look behind, in sober sadness, doubting whether the chances of a safe arrival are not entirely against him", commented *Harper's Weekly*. ". . . Human life is sadly and foolishly squandered." Fortunately, a skilled and dedicated handful of men were getting ready to do something about this grim situation. One of them was George Westinghouse, who, before he had finished, contributed more to the advancement of the railways than any man since Stephenson.

George Westinghouse spent much of his boyhood in his father's shop, a modest family enterprise that produced a line of farm machinery. By the age of 22, he had formed his own company to make railway-repair machinery and switch mechanisms. One day on a sales trip near Troy, New York, he saw a wreck in which two trains had crashed together on a smooth, straight, level stretch of track in broad daylight. He collared a railway employee. "What was the matter?" demanded Westinghouse. "Wouldn't the brakes work?" "Sure," said the man, "but there wasn't time."

The answer set George to brooding. Not long after the wreck, he happened to buy a copy of a magazine called *Living Age*. Thumbing absently through the pages, he suddenly hit upon something. An article told how engineers building the Mont Cenis tunnel in the Alps sent compressed air through 3,000 feet of pipes to drill blasting holes in the rock. That was it. If compressed air could travel 3,000 feet and still punch holes in rock, it could move in pipes through all the coaches of the longest train with sufficient power to clamp shut every brake shoe.

The spectacular debut of air brakes

The test for the first air brake was nothing short of spectacular. Heading out of Pittsburgh with a load of railway officials, Westinghouse's experimental train was coming to a level crossing when a drayman drove his wagon on to the tracks two blocks ahead of the train. With the engine roaring down on him, the drayman lashed the horses, which reared up, flinging the driver on to the track where he lay, like a silent-film heroine, in the path of the engine. In despair, engineer Dan Tate closed

DRIVING THE WHEELS, steam in a locomotive expands against the piston, which in turn works the drive mechanism. For the rearward piston stroke, shown here, steam enters the cylinder (*far left*) by the left port. As it forces the piston rearwards, the piston pushes a connecting rod and a coupling rod to turn the driving wheels. Simultaneously, the piston sweeps spent steam out of the right port to an exhaust opening. The front drive wheel activates the valve rod, pushing forward the sliding valve. This connects the left port to the exhaust system and the right port to the steam pipe, thereby letting the steam come in behind the piston and push it to its original position.

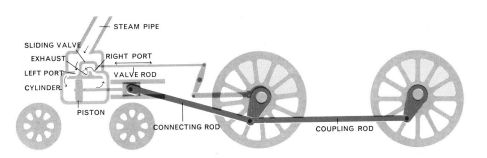

STEAM PIPE

SLIDING VALVE

EXHAUST — RIGHT PORT

LEFT PORT — VALVE ROD

CYLINDER

PISTON

CONNECTING ROD — COUPLING ROD

the valve of his new brake. The train shuddered to a halt, four feet from the prostrate drayman. That should have been enough to convince anyone. And indeed the Pennsylvania Railroad, later joined by a handful of other enlightened roads, installed the new safety device.

But railway tycoons in general were by nature a stubborn, close-fisted lot to whom a new development often seemed like expensive frippery. When Westinghouse enlisted the aid of crusty old Commodore Vanderbilt on equipping the Central's trains with air brakes, the Commodore growled, "Do you pretend to tell me that you could stop trains with wind? I'll give you to understand, young man, that I am too busy to have any time taken up in talking to a damned fool".

At about this time another bright inventor, Major Eli Janney, late of the Confederacy, was having his own troubles getting through to the old-line railwaymen. A supply officer in the railway-poor South, Janney was marooned at the end of the War in the grim role of a penniless clerk in a drapery store in Fairfax County, Virginia. To help to fill the dull hours, Janney set for himself the problem of finding a safer, more efficient coupling device for railway carriages. He found the answer in his hands. By cupping them and hooking together the fingers of the opposite hands, he had the basis of an automatic, knuckle-jointed coupler which could be pushed together but not pulled apart. By closing his thumbs over the outsides of the curved knuckles, he locked the hands so that the fingers would not slide off to one side or the other. Janney whittled a number of models of his coupler, then nailed down the basic design with patents. But like Westinghouse, he got the cold shoulder from most railway executives, who were more interested in saving pennies than lives. "The radical cause of their neglect", wrote the waspish *Harper's New Monthly Magazine* in 1874, "is probably the fact that the lives of railroad employees are inexpensive. . . . A rule of law . . . renders [the railroads] exempt from damages in the case of injuries to employees."

Three against the barons

With the exception of the handful of progressive lines, the railways remained grossly neglectful until the middle of the 1880's, when they came under the combined fire of Westinghouse, Janney and a bearded safety fanatic named Lorenzo Coffin, Commissioner of Railroads for the State of Iowa. By this time Westinghouse had improved his brake, and Janney had strengthened and improved his automatic coupler. As for Coffin, he was enraged at the magnates' shoulder-shrugging, act-of-God attitude towards accidents which sent casualties up to 30,000 per year. By pleas, threats and a deafening peal of oratory, Coffin persuaded the Master Car Builders Association to hold a series of trials on long freight trains. One of those freights was equipped with Westinghouse brakes and Janney couplers. The climax came on a summer day in 1887 outside Burlington, Iowa. "An immense train was hurled down the steep grade into Burlington at 40 miles an hour", wrote one observer. When the brakes were set, "the train came to a standstill *within 500 feet* and

A FORCED RIDE ON AN ENGINE was recommended in this cartoon, which appeared in the British weekly *Punch* in 1853, as the way to make railway executives adopt safety measures. In that year alone, 103 accidents were reported in Britain. In the U.S., as traffic grew and speeds increased to 35 m.p.h., inadequate brakes and haphazard train control also caused mishaps to rise sharply. Newspapers protested with irate editorials, and some States began to formulate safety codes.

with hardly a jar." At the glorious sight, old Lorenzo Coffin burst into tears and shouted, "I am the happiest man in all Creation".

Hardly less happy were George Westinghouse, whose brakes had done the job, and Eli Janney, whose tight-fitting coupler was judged by many observers to be not only marvellous in itself but also the prerequisite for the air brake, which demanded a tight, reliable connection between coaches. Together the brake and coupler were difficult for calloused railway conservatives to ignore. For it gave them the means of silencing the everlasting hue and cry about safety and slaughter on the rails. Far more important to that profit-minded crew, however, it would mean that longer trains could be operated reliably and economically on much tighter schedules. In other words, more freight, more passengers and, after an initial investment for the brakes and couplers, much more revenue. Nevertheless, there was a formidable bloc of objectors. But they were flogged into line in 1893, when President Benjamin Harrison signed the Safety Appliance Act which required automatic couplers and air brakes on all trains. Whereupon Eli Janney settled down to live off his royalties on the sort of Virginia farm which would soothe the soul of any retired Confederate major who had served 20 years as a draper's clerk and poor inventor.

Not so George Westinghouse. Here was the archetype of the 19th-century captain of industry, who could put together big corporations like the Westinghouse Air Brake Company and, later, the mammoth Westinghouse Electric Corporation and run the business with the same sure instinct that he used in perfecting his original invention. "Like a lion in the forest," reported an awed contemporary, "he breathed deep and with delight the smoky air of his factories. . . . He was transformed into a giant when confronted with difficulties which seemed insurmountable."

Signals, switches and control towers

Having cleared the track of one set of difficulties, Westinghouse now hurled himself at another aspect of railway operation which had lain too long in neglect: the business of signalling, switching points, and traffic control. By 1891 he had a patent on an elaborate system of track signals and points, actuated by compressed air and monitored from a central control tower, which told every passing locomotive engineer when the stretch of line ahead was clear and when it was not. Later, Westinghouse and others refined and extended the system so that whole networks of main line with their complex shunting-yards (*pages 74-75*) could be run with swift security from a single electronic control board; trains which accidentally ran through "STOP" signals would have their brakes applied by automatic devices; and a system of checks and balances would make it impossible for points ever to be set the wrong way to receive an oncoming train.

With the safe and efficient movement of their trains thus assured, the railways turned a freshly critical eye on their source of power. For all its faithful service and appealing personality, the steam-engine was a temperamental creature which required too much care and feeding. A freight locomotive had to stop every 30 miles or so to take on water, every 100 miles to fill up with coal. Even the most sophisticated passenger engine, equipped with a scoop to pick up water in motion from a pan between the rails, had to pull into the roundhouse every 230 miles to have its ashpan cleaned and to rest its crew. The busiest road locomotive spent less than a quarter of its hours earning its keep; the remainder of the time it was being expensively pampered.

Electricity challenges steam

A few railways tried introducing electrical power generated in a central plant. And at first this seemed to be the answer. The electric locomotive took current either through an overhead wire or through a third rail. The power went into smooth-operating traction motors, which delivered more muscle per pound than the steamer. Furthermore, the electrics required no warm-ups, no six-hour turn-around, no water stops and no mountains of coal in bunkers along the track. Where they ran through residential zones, there was little noise and no filth. In tunnels, the absence of gases and blinding smoke allowed a terminal like Grand Central in New York to increase its hourly traffic rate by 50 per cent after the lines were electrified. And, wonder of wonders, when coasting downhill, with the motors idling and in gear, the rotation of the wheels transmitted energy back through the gears to turn the motors so that they not only slowed the train but also became dynamos which fed electricity back into the power line. "The first railroad that electrifies for the thousand miles between here and New York," predicted a Chicago traffic man, "is going to get all the rich passenger business. Not a big portion of it, but every bit."

Despite its clean power and efficiency, however, electricity generated from a central plant cost too much to install on all but the busiest sections, where the traffic density could make up for the high price of stringing wire or laying a third rail. (Seventy years after the appearance of the first commercially operating electric train in 1895 on the Nantasket Beach Branch of the New York, New Haven and Hartford line, only 1,814 miles of U.S. track was electrified, most of it urban and suburban routes, and in tunnels.) The real need was for an engine which had all the good qualities of the electric engine, but could get along without third rails, overhead wires or central power plants.

That engine appeared in 1925 when the Central Railroad of New Jersey put into service the first so-called diesel-electric locomotive to run on U.S. track. In a locomotive like this, the diesel engine, running on vaporized oil, turns a dynamo which provides power for electric motors geared to its axles. The first diesel on the Jersey Central was a small, 300-horsepower switcher. But its descendants ultimately grew into 3,500- and even 7,500-horsepower brutes capable of hauling over 5,000 tons of freight 1,610 miles from St. Paul, Minnesota, to Wenatchee, Washington, without a change of engines, or a string of passenger carriages over the 1,048 miles between Chicago and Denver at speeds up to 90 m.p.h. On a run of this kind—of any kind, for that matter—the diesel-electric is a marvel of economy. Just two tablespoons of fuel oil can move a ton a mile. Today, 99 per cent of all U.S. rail freight and passenger traffic is carried behind diesel-electric engines. The rest of it moves by straight electricity. Unfortunately for those who remember earlier times, there is no more steam in mainline service.

But no amount of diesel efficiency—or light, streamlined passenger trains or 100-ton covered-hopper freight cars or any of the other thousands of mechanical improvements brought in after the 1920's—could make up for the railways' fundamental inadequacies. For the rails were not, in themselves, a complete system of land transportation. They were only one part of a system. Railway trains were—and are—superb for moving bulk freight between two points, preferably two relatively distant points. They are also quite effective in transporting masses of people, at least 800 to a train, from one fixed point to another. But if one of those people wants to be at the hairdresser's four miles from home in Evanston, Illinois, at 9.30, and another has to clock in at a factory 20 miles on the other side of Chicago at 8.00, there is no way they can both make it on a single train. By the same token, if a shipper has a load of diverse items for house-to-house delivery, the train is impossible.

The nadir of the iron horse

What that shipper and that lady heading for the hairdresser's need is a means of individual transportation—something they can drive themselves or conveniently hire. Something that leaves when they want it to leave and goes where they want it to go. Something like a motor-car, or motor lorry. In 1923, there were already 13 million cars and nearly two million lorries in America, and the motor-car had gone a long way towards filling the gaps between the rail lines with an effective means of individual transportation. Very soon, trucks would begin to cut into inter-city freight traffic. Cars and buses (and ultimately aeroplanes) would whittle down the rail-borne share of inter-city passengers below 2 per cent. And the railways, once the focal point of the most dramatic change in the whole history of overland transportation, would be glacially slow in rising to meet the challenge of this new technology.

Those few passengers who still moved by rail would, indeed, suffer from "tired, inadequate transportation". As for the movement of goods, freight cars might languish on sidings for weeks, waiting to be individually weighed on balance scales designed before the turn of the century; the air-brake hoses on every train would still be coupled and recoupled by hand the way they were 85 years ago. Eventually, the railways would commence a great leap forward to meet the demands for mobility of the space age. But it would be some time before they began to close the technology gap, and even longer before rails and motor vehicles learned to coexist, peacefully and profitably, as two parts of an over-arching system of land transportation.

The Way to Run
a Railway

In San Bernardino, California, a refrigerator van loaded with oranges is coupled on to a Santa Fe freight train, heading east. For 2,163 miles, all the complex technology of a modern rail system is brought to bear on that van. It is pulled by four diesel locomotives with a combined strength of 10,000 horsepower; it is stopped by air brakes three times as powerful; it is whisked past slower trains in the very teeth of oncoming traffic; twice it is unhitched, sorted out by remote control, and made part of a new train. Less than 70 hours after leaving San Bernardino, the van-load of fruit rolls up to a grocery warehouse in Chicago, its destination. The entire cost of the journey: about one new pence per pound of oranges.

Much of the technology that makes such trips possible has been in existence a long time. The flanged wheel (*right*) that guides trains along steel rails was used on mining carts before 1600. Automatic signalling came into wide use in the 1890's. Since then other improvements have gradually been introduced. In the 1930's the railways adopted long-distance electric switching. Computers are now employed to shuttle coaches from one train to another; some railway men even foresee fully automated trains pulled by crewless locomotives.

STEEL MEETS STEEL
The two basic elements of the railway are a T-shaped steel rail that can support loads of up to 17 tons per wheel, and the steel wheel, which has a rim, or flange, to guide it along the rail. For easy turning, the wheels are arranged in groups of four on structures called trucks, as on the caboose in the background. All four wheels on the truck pivot as a unit.

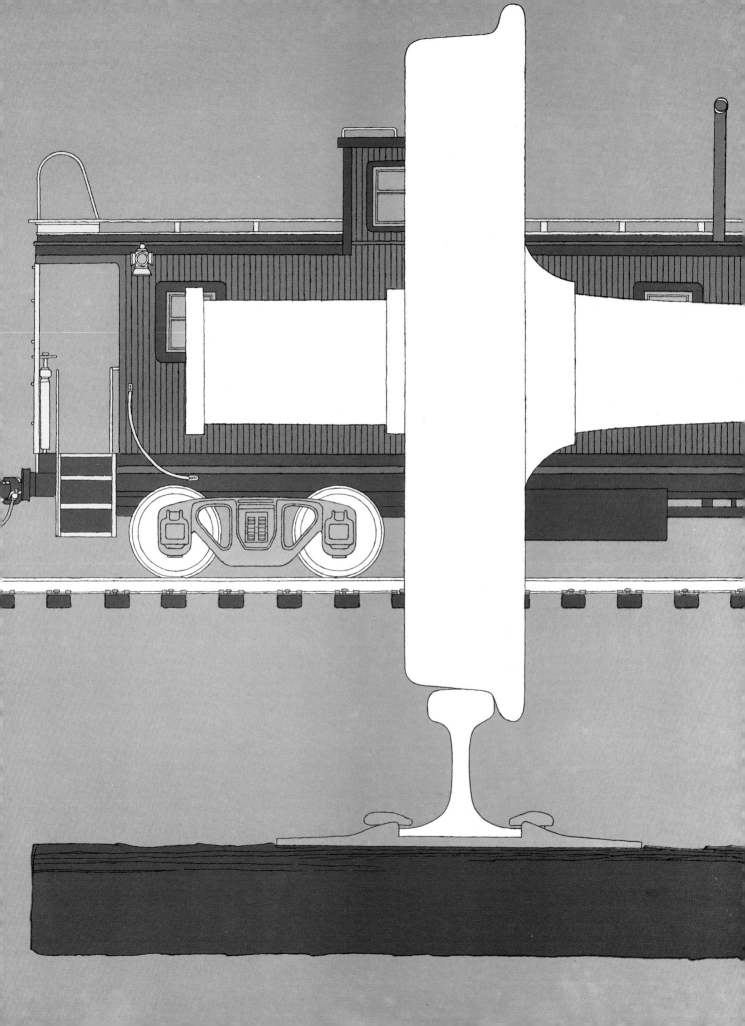

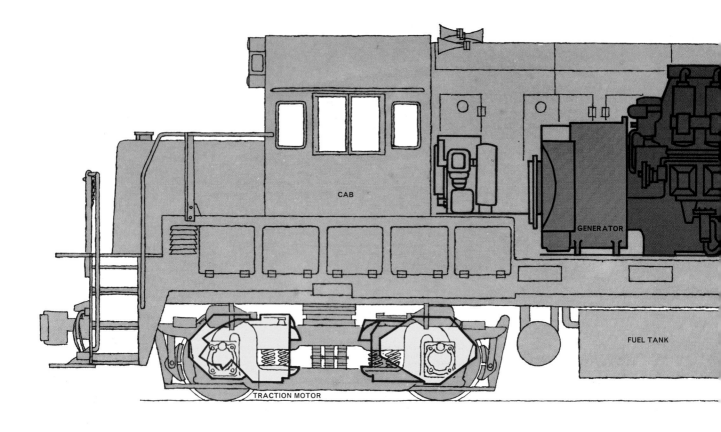

CAB

GENERATOR

FUEL TANK

TRACTION MOTOR

The Brute Power of the Diesel

Blunt-nosed, massive, its very lines exuding power, the diesel-electric locomotive is the workhorse that keeps the steel wheels of modern freight trains rolling. The engine shown above weighs a quarter of a million pounds and develops 2,500 horsepower. It can steadily exert as much as 75,000 pounds of pull on a train and cruise along at 80 m.p.h. Diesel engines like this one comprise 99 per cent of the locomotives used in the U.S. today; the figure was less than 1 per cent in 1940.

The reason for the diesel supremacy is simple: it is the most efficient internal-combustion engine ever devised. It uses inexpensive oil, much like that consumed in home furnaces, and this oil ignites by itself, without the need for a spark, as the cylinders' great compression generates tremendous heat. The high temperature of combustion enables diesel engines to convert 25 per cent of the available energy of the fuel into useful work —a big jump in efficiency over the wasteful 7 per cent conversion rate of steam locomotives. Because of this efficiency, a 16-cylinder, V-shaped engine like the one shown here can pull one ton of freight one mile for just a little more than a penny.

Cheap it is, and powerful. But the diesel locomotive has another important advantage: it needs no intricate motor-car-style clutch-and-gear system to regulate driving force and transmit it to the wheels. Instead, the energy from the diesel is converted into electricity for motors that turn the wheels. This electric drive can also help to brake the train. To slow down, the engineer switches circuits so that the motors no longer turn the wheels; instead, the wheels are forced to turn the motors. This effort reduces the speed of the train.

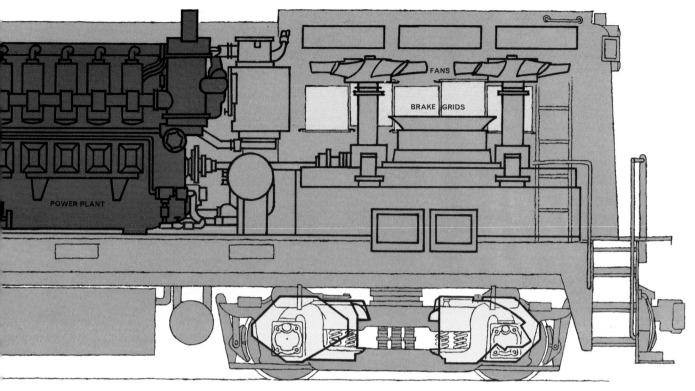

AN X-RAY VIEW OF A DIESEL

The General Electric U25B diesel locomotive, whose innards are shown above, is employed by many railways for high-speed freight runs. Drawing fuel oil from a 2,400-gallon tank slung under the locomotive's belly, the diesel power plant (*brown*) drives a generator (*red*) which can produce about 1,860 kilowatts of electricity—enough to light 50 homes. This heavy current powers 4 axle-mounted motors (*yellow*), each transmitting 625 horsepower. The same motors serve for braking when the flick of a switch changes them into wheel-driven generators; the current that they then produce is used up by converting it into heat in many toaster-like grids (*orange*), cooled by fans, in the rear of the diesel.

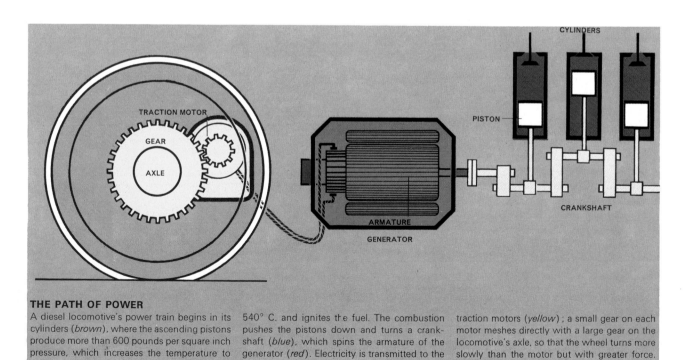

THE PATH OF POWER

A diesel locomotive's power train begins in its cylinders (*brown*), where the ascending pistons produce more than 600 pounds per square inch pressure, which increases the temperature to 540° C. and ignites the fuel. The combustion pushes the pistons down and turns a crankshaft (*blue*), which spins the armature of the generator (*red*). Electricity is transmitted to the traction motors (*yellow*); a small gear on each motor meshes directly with a large gear on the locomotive's axle, so that the wheel turns more slowly than the motor but with greater force.

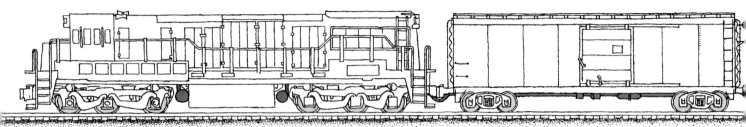

Braking
a Behemoth

Hurtling along at 80 m.p.h., the average goods train possesses the destructive energy of about 3,000 sticks of dynamite. Yet the train can be halted and its monstrous energy released by a few gentle puffs of air, which activate its brakes.

The system that accomplishes this feat was invented in the 1860's by the prolific Pittsburgh engineer, George Westinghouse, who also pioneered interlocking block signals for railways (*pages 72-73*). The air brakes in use today are nearly foolproof. Unlike earlier systems, they do not rely on a fallible central source of compressed air to activate them; every car has its own air tank. Furthermore, the brakes are applied not by an increase in air pressure, but by a decrease; thus if an air hose linking cars (*above, red*) springs a leak, or the cars become disconnected, the reduction in air pressure automatically stops the train instead of letting it roll free.

The brain of this fail-safe system is a complex control valve underneath each car, which meters compressed air from tank to brake. This valve is actuated by pressure differences. It keeps the brake off as long as the pressure in the air supply pipe is the same as the pressure in the tank. If pipe pressure drops slightly below tank pressure, this small difference is routed by the valve to the brake, applying it gently. But if the engineer hits his lever for a panic stop, suddenly releasing all the air pressure from the pipe, the brake slams on hard.

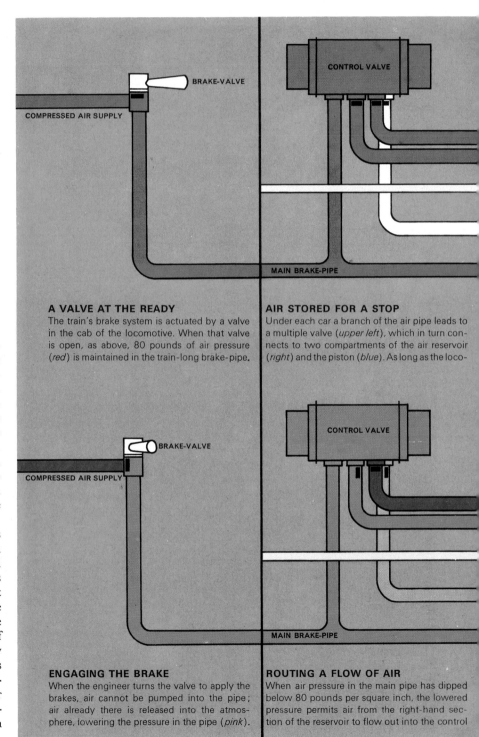

A VALVE AT THE READY
The train's brake system is actuated by a valve in the cab of the locomotive. When that valve is open, as above, 80 pounds of air pressure (*red*) is maintained in the train-long brake-pipe.

AIR STORED FOR A STOP
Under each car a branch of the air pipe leads to a multiple valve (*upper left*), which in turn connects to two compartments of the air reservoir (*right*) and the piston (*blue*). As long as the loco-

ENGAGING THE BRAKE
When the engineer turns the valve to apply the brakes, air cannot be pumped into the pipe; air already there is released into the atmosphere, lowering the pressure in the pipe (*pink*).

ROUTING A FLOW OF AIR
When air pressure in the main pipe has dipped below 80 pounds per square inch, the lowered pressure permits air from the right-hand section of the reservoir to flow out into the control

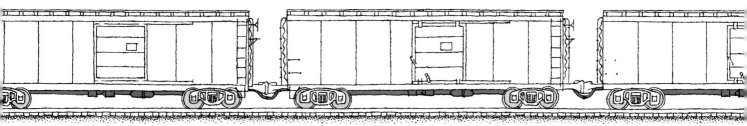

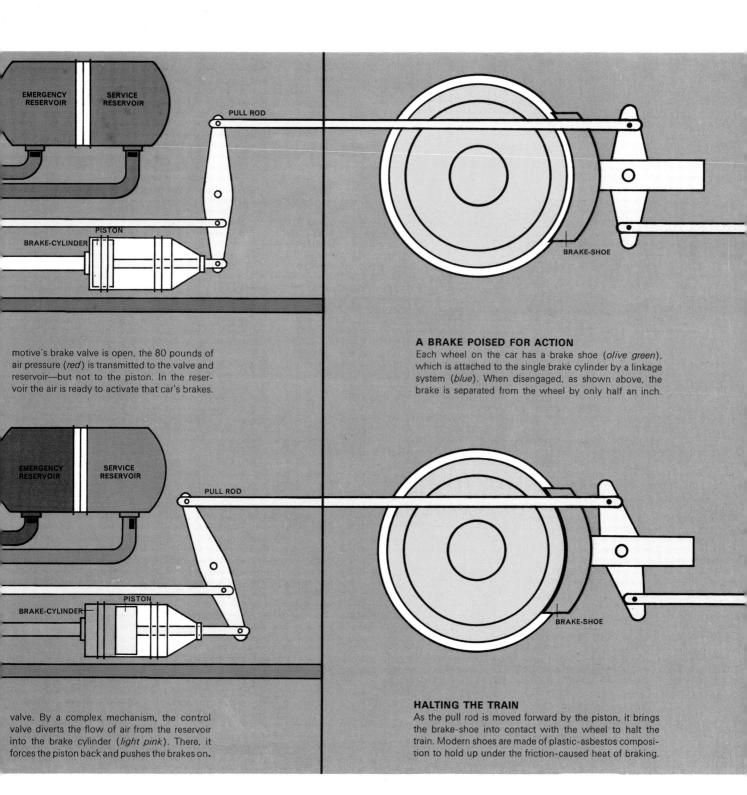

motive's brake valve is open, the 80 pounds of air pressure (*red*) is transmitted to the valve and reservoir—but not to the piston. In the reservoir the air is ready to activate that car's brakes.

A BRAKE POISED FOR ACTION

Each wheel on the car has a brake shoe (*olive green*), which is attached to the single brake cylinder by a linkage system (*blue*). When disengaged, as shown above, the brake is separated from the wheel by only half an inch.

valve. By a complex mechanism, the control valve diverts the flow of air from the reservoir into the brake cylinder (*light pink*). There, it forces the piston back and pushes the brakes on.

HALTING THE TRAIN

As the pull rod is moved forward by the piston, it brings the brake-shoe into contact with the wheel to halt the train. Modern shoes are made of plastic-asbestos composition to hold up under the friction-caused heat of braking.

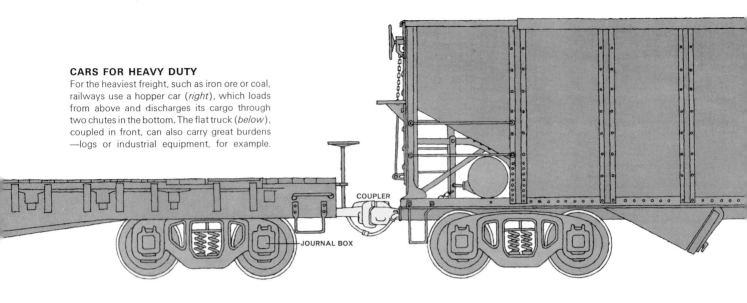

CARS FOR HEAVY DUTY

For the heaviest freight, such as iron ore or coal, railways use a hopper car (*right*), which loads from above and discharges its cargo through two chutes in the bottom. The flat truck (*below*), coupled in front, can also carry great burdens —logs or industrial equipment, for example.

COUPLER

JOURNAL BOX

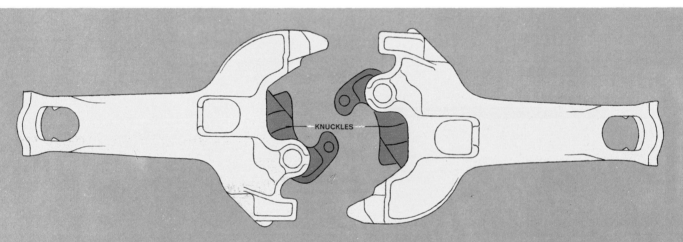

KNUCKLES

AN AUTOMATIC GRIP OF STEEL

Two goods-carriage couplers (*yellow*) are shown approaching each other above, with their clasps or "knuckles" (*red*) open. When the couplers meet, the knuckles touch and then, acting like fingers clasping each other, they pivot into a gripping position (*below*). At this point, a lock inside each coupler automatically drops into place and prevents further movement of the knuckles. The couplers will not release unless the locks are pulled up by a trainman. These couplers sustain so many impacts in goods yards over the years that they grow shorter by up to $\frac{5}{8}$ of an inch.

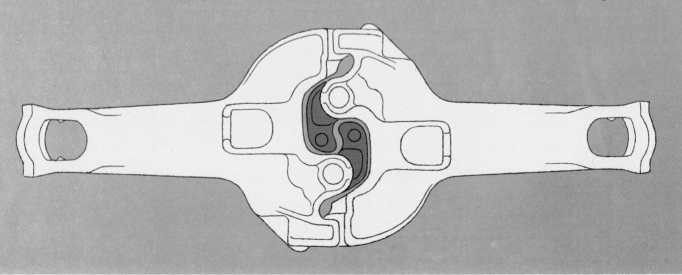

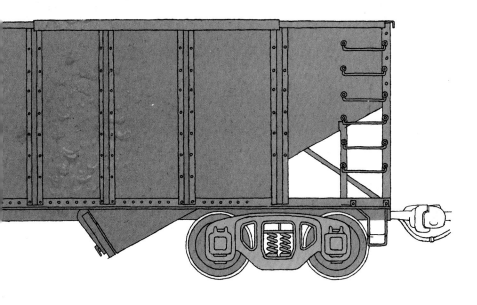

Where the Forces Focus

A goods train carries a prodigious burden, more by far than any other means of overland transportation. A single coach like the one shown on these pages may weigh 100 tons when it is loaded with iron ore. Such weights produce crushing forces in two directions: downwards through the wheels, and horizontally along the train.

The horizontal forces focus at the couplers, or linking mechanisms between cars (*far left*), which must be built to withstand herculean games of tug-of-war alternating with shattering impacts. If a coupler is situated near the front of a train, it has to pull the load of all the cars behind it—up to 300,000 pounds of tension. In the process of coupling cars in goods yards, the force is reversed and the coupler must withstand up to a million pounds of compressive force when the coaches connect.

Strength and durability are not enough, however. The couplers must also be so sensitive that they will clasp together automatically when goods coaches nudge against each other at only one mile an hour. This automatic coupling gives a valuable bonus: men no longer have to stand between coaches during coupling as they once did, because now the couplers do all the work themselves.

The downward forces exerted by a heavy goods train focus on the journal box on each wheel (*left*), where the weight of the car and its contents rides on a film of oil only two ten-thousandths of an inch thick. In older journal boxes this film often became clogged with bits of dirt or with threads from the mop-like cotton packing that dispensed the oil; clogging caused the rotating axle to heat up, throw sparks and sometimes melt. But such breakdowns, called "hot boxes", are now rare. Modern journal boxes are sealed, and have oil-dispensing pads of tough synthetic rubber. They will carry the coaches two million miles without a hot box.

RIDING ON A FILM OF OIL

The journal box (*olive green*) is the juncture of the downward-pressing load and the axle. Inside the box a piece of brass called the journal bearing (*red*) rests above the axle, held in place by another piece of metal called the wedge (*orange*). A synthetic rubber pad (*yellow*) in the box is soaked with oil. As the axle turns, it brushes the threads of the pad and is coated with oil. The bearing rides on this friction-reducing film. Every 1,000 miles or so, the lid on the left side of the box is lifted and oil is added.

Leap-Frogging a Slow Goods Train

Modern car traffic requires as many as eight parallel lanes of highway, but railways can keep their trains moving across country along only two sets of tracks, one for each direction. Faster trains pass slower ones by switching into the face of oncoming traffic and then back on to the original track. This tricky manœuvre is made possible by a system of automatic switches and signals called Centralized Traffic Control or CTC.

From a central control room, the CTC dispatcher co-ordinates the movements of dozens of trains electrically. Sitting in front of a console he sees the trains in his sector—which may cover hundreds of miles—as lights inching along a miniaturized diagram of the tracks. Armed with a list of train priorities, the dispatcher presses buttons that set signals and throw switches to manœuvre passenger and freight trains through situations like the one shown here, in which an express "leap-frogs" a slower train. In the diagram the actual distances are reduced and, as indicated by the changing position of the railway shed (*yellow*), the action moves to the right.

THE WEAVING PATH OF AN EXPRESS

Centralized Traffic Control gets a fast goods train past slower trains by flashing green, yellow or red lights inside each locomotive cab and also on a trackside tower. In Stage 1 (*top*) an east-bound express (*orange*) begins to overtake a goods train (*brown*) on the east-bound track, while a west-bound train (*blue*) approaches on the other track; all three trains are under full-speed (*green*) signals. In Stage 2, CTC maintains the green signal to the west-bound train, and tells the east-bound express to proceed on to the opposite track with caution (*yellow-green light*). Meanwhile the slow goods train, still given a green light, travels at its normal speed. In Stage 3 the east-bound express passes the slow goods train at full speed, heading straight into the path of a second train (*green*) travelling west. This train is warned by a yellow light to stop when it reaches the switch at the point indicated by the red triangle. In Stage 4 the express crosses back to its original track, proceeding through the switch with a caution (*yellow-green*) light, while the west-bound train is halted, and the slow goods train is warned by a yellow light to stop when it reaches the point marked by the red triangle.

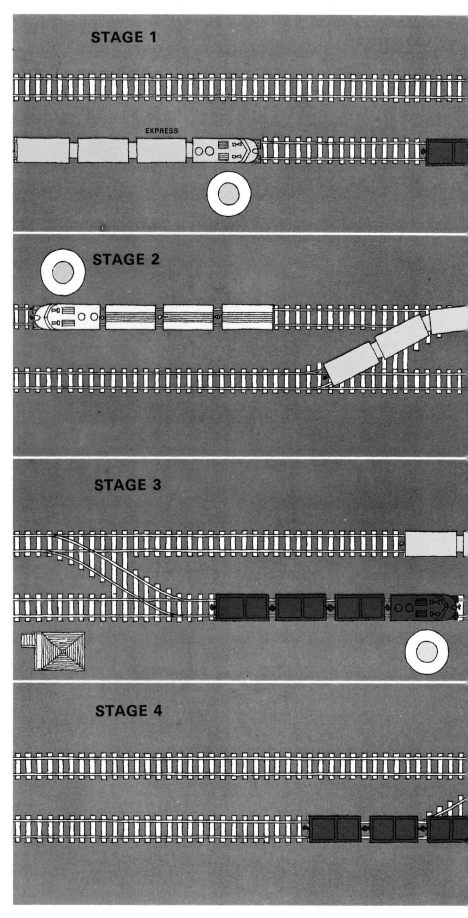

STAGE 1

EXPRESS

STAGE 2

STAGE 3

STAGE 4

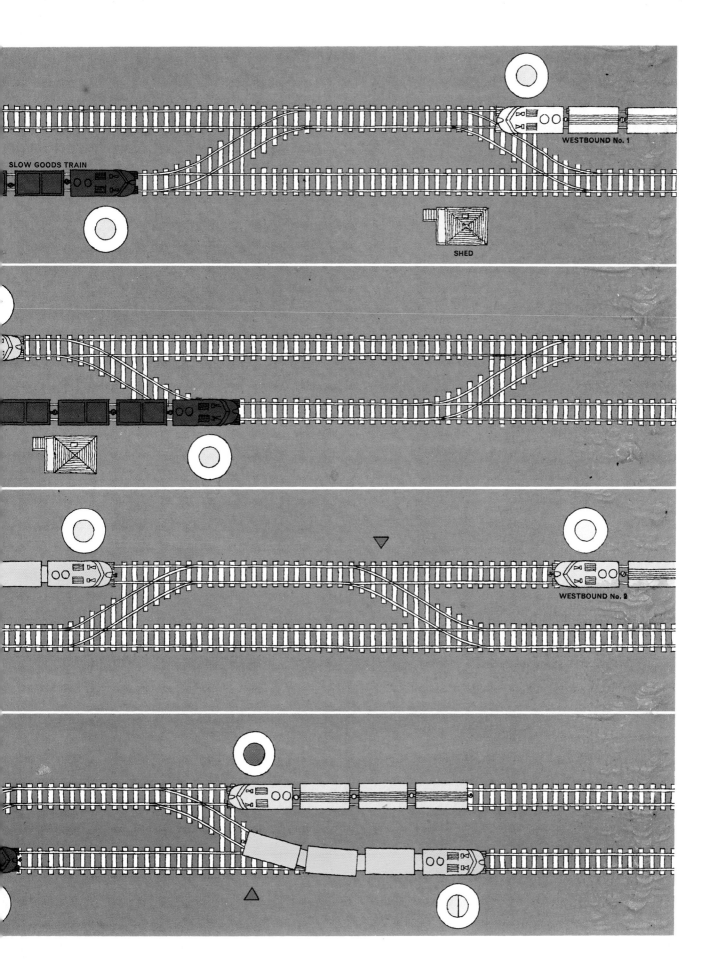

SLOW GOODS TRAIN

WESTBOUND No. 1

SHED

WESTBOUND No. 2

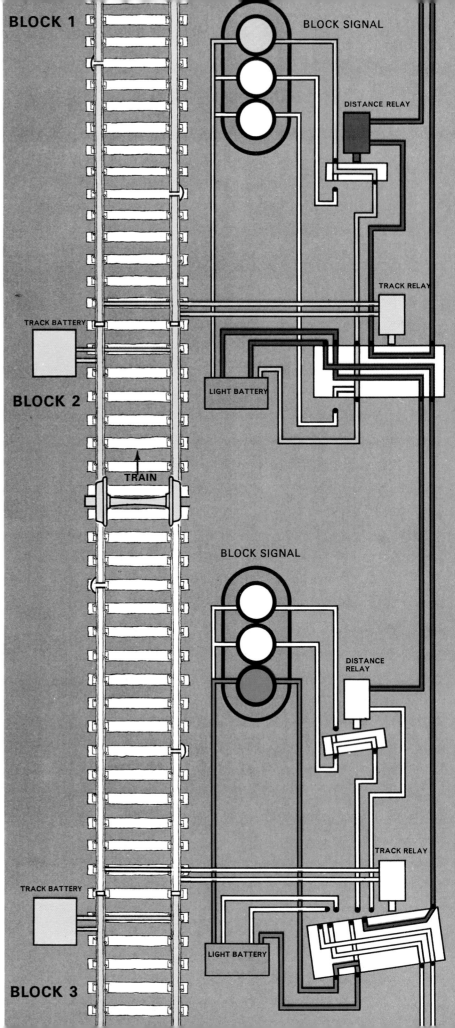

BLOCK SIGNAL

DISTANCE RELAY

TRACK RELAY

TRACK BATTERY

LIGHT BATTERY

BLOCK 2

TRAIN

BLOCK SIGNAL

DISTANCE RELAY

TRACK RELAY

TRACK BATTERY

LIGHT BATTERY

BLOCK 3

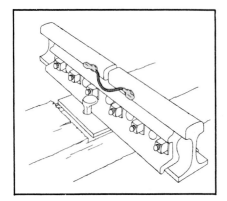

CURRENT-CARRYING RAILS

The track itself is a crucial element in the electrical circuits that operate modern train signals. A short wire (*orange*) carries battery-produced electricity over the gap where two rails meet.

HOW TRAIN SIGNALS WORK

The signal system shown here controls train traffic in four "blocks" of track. Each block has two batteries located in boxes near the track. The track battery sends current (*orange*) up and down the track and across it to the track relay, keeping it closed. The light battery delivers current to the block signal—in this case to the green light, instructing that the next block up ahead is vacant. As long as there is no train in that block, current (*brown*) flows down through to a block 1 switch known as a distance relay; this keeps the distance relay closed and permits the current to flow to the block 1 green light. Farther down the track, a train (*indicated by two wheels*) is travelling through block 2. Its wheels cut off the current to the track relay in that block, causing the relay to drop down and close a circuit (*red*) that sends current to the red light.

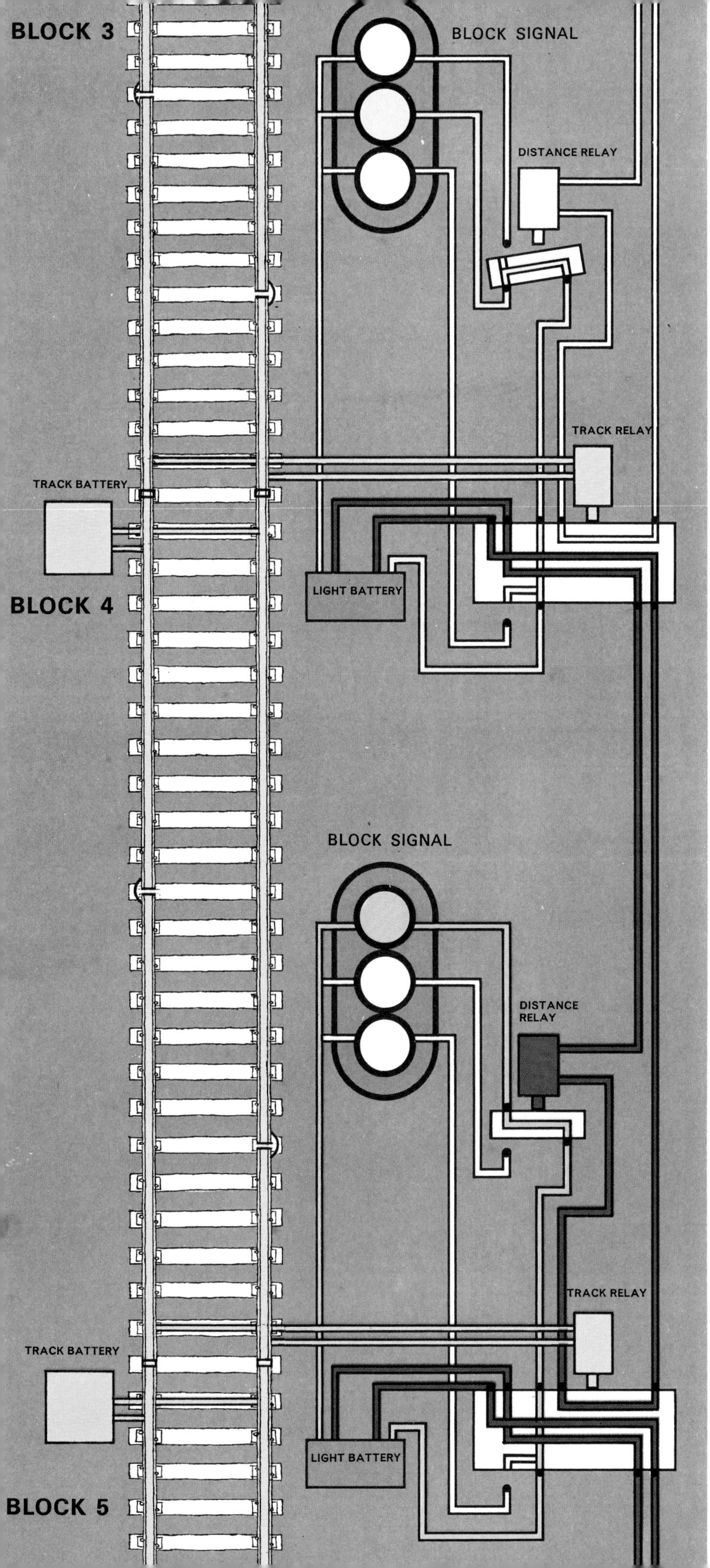

BLOCK 3

BLOCK SIGNAL

DISTANCE RELAY

TRACK RELAY

TRACK BATTERY

BLOCK 4

LIGHT BATTERY

BLOCK SIGNAL

DISTANCE RELAY

TRACK RELAY

TRACK BATTERY

LIGHT BATTERY

BLOCK 5

Traffic That Regulates Itself

By the time the engineer of a speeding goods train spots the caboose of a stalled train ahead of him, he is usually too close to stop. To extend the warning beyond the limits of the engine-driver's eyesight, and thus make it possible for heavy traffic to travel quickly and safely over the rails, elaborate electric signalling systems have been developed.

In these systems trains automatically leave warning messages in their wakes by triggering signal lights beside the tracks (and, on some lines, inside the locomotive cabs as well). More than 100,000 miles of U.S. track are now divided into signal "blocks" —stretches of track 1 to 15 miles long that must never be occupied by more than one train at a time. The diagram on the left shows a sequence of four such blocks. When the tracks are clear, current flows through the tracks in all these blocks and all lights are green. But when a train comes along, it breaks circuits as it goes through each block. This actuates red and yellow lights which tell trains behind to stop or slow down.

IN THE WAKE OF THE TRAIN
The signal in block 3 (*top*) indicates caution because a train occupies block 2 (*opposite page*). No current flows from the track relay in block 2 to the distance relay in block 3, leaving the block 3 distance relay down (i.e., open). But since no train occupies block 3, current from the track battery can flow to move the block 3 track relay up. This leads current (*yellow*) from the light battery through the block 3 distance relay to the yellow "go slow" light. Because the track relay in block 3 is up, current (*brown*) flows down from that block to the distance relay in block 4. Here, because both relays are up, the circuit to the green light is closed, turning that light on, just as in block 1. All the other empty blocks behind block 4 will also display a green signal—until another train comes along to trigger the same sequence of events.

Sorting Freight by Electronics

A goods truck can get from one place to any other along the rails that criss-cross the U.S.—but, like a hitch-hiker, it seldom goes the full route on a single ride. For example, a truck carrying plywood from Portland, Oregon, to Eldred, Pennsylvania, couples on to five separate trains, riding two branch lines and three major rail arteries across the nation.

When it reaches Conway, Pennsylvania, near Pittsburgh, the covered wagon—along with the 50 to 100 cars that arrive with it—goes through a highly efficient sorting-out procedure in a goods yard. One by one, trucks from the incoming train are pushed up

a low hill called "the hump" and allowed to roll down across a succession of points set so as to guide each truck to its outward-bound train. In the past, cars were sometimes derailed because they rolled too fast, or were stranded in the yard because they rolled too slowly. But in modern goods yards the weight and rolling rate of each car are electronically measured and fed to a computer, which instructs an automatic braking system along the tracks to slow the truck just enough for gentle coupling. Using this sophisticated technology, some goods yards can sort 6,000 cars a day in an uninterrupted flow.

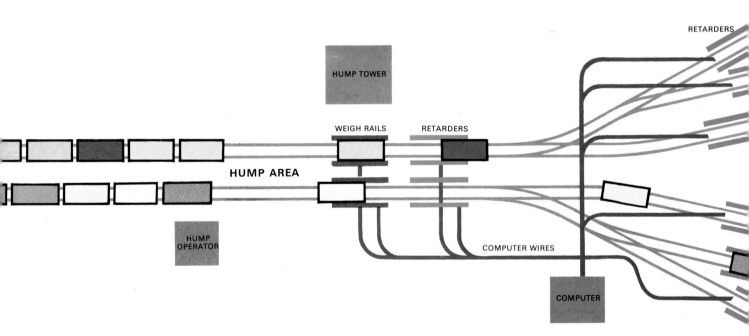

A COMPUTERIZED FREIGHT YARD

The diagram above shows how the trucks of two trains (*left*), arriving at the Conway goods yard near Pittsburgh, are sorted out according to destination (indicated by colour). As the cars are uncoupled (*left*), a hump operator electronically sets switches to route each car to

the proper train. A special section of rail weighs each car (*directly above*); with this information a computer calculates how much braking force it requires as it rolls down the hump. Signals are then sent by wires (*brown lines*) to set the retarder mechanisms flanking the tracks.

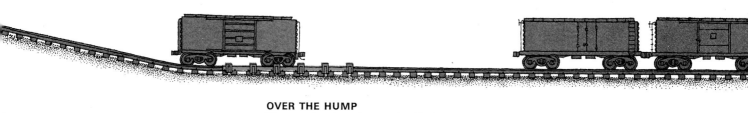

OVER THE HUMP

When goods trains arrive at a classification yard for sorting, they are pushed up to a hump and uncoupled. Each coach then rolls freely downhill until it reaches the first set of retarders (*red*) which slows the car by squeezing metal shoes against its wheels. Rolling the rest of the way downhill, the car is slowed once again by another set of retarders so that it will be going less than four m.p.h. when it couples to its outward-bound train. The retarders are so accurately controlled by the computer that a car's speed can be adjusted to within one-tenth of a mile an hour.

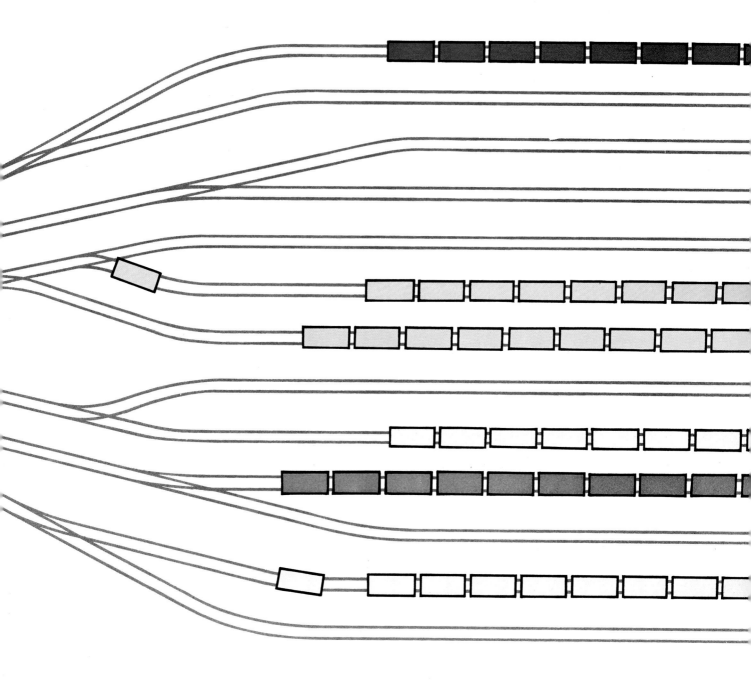

4

From Flivver
to Fastback

Recalling the glories of once-famous motor cars,
this collection of old nameplates commemo-
rates a few of the 3,000-odd makes manufactured in the U.S. since the 1890's, among them
the Stutz, Locomobile, Chandler and Packard.

A MOTOR-CAR is a superb instrument—quick, powerful, instantly responsive. At a touch of the hand, a ton and a half of gleaming steel begins to purr with the power of more than a hundred horses. The feather-like movement of a short lever makes the machine roll backwards or forwards. With a twist of the wheel, it can turn in a circle with a tight 20-foot radius. At close quarters it can creep at one mile per hour; and a few specially designed machines have sped over a test course at more than 600 m.p.h. Cruising at 60 m.p.h., it generates about the same amount of kinetic energy as a 75-millimetre artillery shell. Yet with the touch of a foot on the brake pedal, this hurtling mass can be stopped in six seconds. The motor-car will carry one person or six over any reasonable surface from a dirt track to a concrete highway, and can easily climb a gradient of over 30 per cent. Its big brother, the truck, can wrestle 100 tons of gravel out of a deep pit, transport an intercontinental missile filled with delicate electronic instruments, carry 5,000 gallons of hydrochloric acid through a city street, or deliver a refrigerated load of melons, field-fresh, to a grocer on the other side of town or the other side of the continent. It is by all odds the most convenient, comfortable, flexible means ever devised for moving an individual or his produce from one place to another in his own time and at his own speed. Yet there are those who love it not.

In 1900, when there were only a handful of horseless carriages and a few embryo trucks rattling around, farmers planted broken bottles, knives and nails, points up, in the roads to keep the noisy, smelly machines from bothering decent folk and peaceful farm animals. (The year before, Mr. H. H. Bliss of New York became the first traffic fatality when he paused to help a lady off a tram-car and was struck down by a passing motor-car). Six years later, after Ransom E. Olds had begun mass-producing the first low-priced car, a one-cylinder runabout memorialized as My Merry Oldsmobile, Woodrow Wilson, who was later to become President of the United States, looked loathingly at the rising tide of rubber-tyred transport and grunted, "Nothing has spread socialistic feeling more than the use of the automobile . . . a picture of the arrogance of wealth".

One car builder, the Woods Motor Vehicle Company, responded by pointing out in a catalogue how much its cars looked like good old-fashioned horse-drawn carriages, thereby "relieving the occupants of any sense of embarrassment or conspicuousness". But none of the public relations practised by the car industry then or since has managed to camouflage the real problems created by the motor-car. Today, in the U.S., with more than 100 million vehicles on the road and Detroit selling 10 million or so new ones in some years, sins committed by the motor vehicle include everything from traffic snarls to carbon-monoxide smog to the proliferation of highway posters to the awful tragedy of 50,000 deaths per year.

In spite of its social shortcomings, however, and even its lethal properties, the motor vehicle is a magnificent engineering achievement which deserves a good deal more praise than it gets. In the 90-odd years since its birth, it has evolved through a series of refinements represented by 600,000 patents in the United States alone. In recent years the U.S. government and a handful of large universities have mounted imposing research projects aimed at developing the motor-car's ultimate replacement. But none have come close to finding anything better.

"An auto is a wonderful thing", said a dean of the U.S. Massachusetts Institute of Technology, as he wound up the preliminary phase of a three-year search for the vehicle of the future. "When you consider it costs only a dollar a pound, with all that precision, I don't know anything else you can buy for that price."

From tons of steel to slices of cork

A typical American car is made up of some 12,000 basic parts whose materials are got together from all over the world—more than a ton of steel from American mills, bauxite ore from Surinam for the aluminium grillwork, thin slices of Portuguese cork for gaskets, Bolivian asbestos for brake linings. Welded, bolted, riveted and glued into one piece, the car weighs close to 4,000 pounds on the average in the intermediate-sized models; and the average price for these models is close to £1,600. Despite its complex structure, the motor-car remains so easy to operate that nearly anyone can drive it. The U.S. has over 100 million licensed drivers ranging from the 14-year-olds who can get special permits in South Dakota to weak-eyed old ladies of 90 in Kansas, where, until a few years ago, 10 per cent of the people receiving aid to the blind were licensed.

To carry this immense number and variety of highway drivers, U.S. manufacturers turn out some 1,500 different types of vehicles. Among them is one, a versatile hybrid called the sedan pick-up, which is particularly useful as an example of the modern American car. As the name implies, this unique machine is half passenger-sedan, half pick-up van, with a loading bay and tail-board where the rear seat and boot of an ordinary saloon would be. Sometimes the pick-up carries passengers; sometimes it carries a load of goods. As it shuttles to and fro between the world of passengers and that of goods, all its major components—electrical circuits, engine, transmission and differential—must meet all the demands made of a passenger car and many of those endured by a van. It is these demands that dictate the ways in which a motor vehicle is designed. To understand these demands, and the ways in which they are met through the engineering of the multipurpose sedan pick-up, is to understand the basic design and function of all motor vehicles.

"When you build the average family car, you know what you want it to do", says a top engineer at General Motors, which annually makes about one-quarter of the vehicles in all the world. "You're going to carry people (the average is about two per trip) with maybe some luggage and groceries. The load factors are not very harsh. And that car goes four or five miles on each trip."

To move any car any distance at all requires a twisting force that en-

THE WAY GEARS WORK in increasing driving force, or torque, is explained in the diagrams above. A gear acts like a lever (*top*), whose torque depends on two factors: the amount of force (indicated by a weight) applied to one end of the lever, and the distance of the force from the lever's pivot point (*blue*). If one lever presses against a second lever (*middle*) that is twice as long, the second lever's torque will be twice that of the first lever. The meshed teeth of two gears serve as paired levers. The large gear at the bottom—twice the size of the small gear—doubles the driving force exerted by the small gear, but halves its rotating speed.

gineers call torque and measure in units of pounds-feet. On a smooth, level concrete road, the engine must supply to the driving wheels seven pounds-feet of torque for every 1,000 pounds of weight in order to keep the vehicle moving. The six-cylinder sedan pick-up, whose body weight is comparable to that of an intermediate-sized car, therefore needs 23 pounds-feet of drive-shaft torque to roll on the level. But to go up a 30 per cent gradient with half a ton of cargo in the loading bay (the same weight as six passengers in an ordinary car), the engine must supply the wheels with 1,650 pounds-feet of torque.

And, of course, the faster the car goes, the greater the torque that must be supplied—a torque of 30 pounds-feet is needed at 20 miles an hour, 93 pounds-feet at 80. Providing amounts of torque for hills and varying velocities is not the only requirement the engine must meet. To maintain the high torque required at high speeds, the engine must produce energy at a faster rate. Its ability to do this is indicated by the familiar horsepower rating—the faster the car goes, the more horsepower is needed. At 60 m.p.h. it spins at 2,650 r.p.m. to supply the 30 h.p. the car demands at that speed. The top capacity of the sedan pick-up's engine is 110 h.p., at 3,800 r.p.m., giving the driver an adequate cushion of speed both for emergencies and for his ego.

"With a car," says Ford's chief design engineer, "you must build in extra power for acceleration, to give the car agility for passing, for going up hills, for emergencies; and I know we are accused of selling horse-power to please the youth. Some of those youths, I'm afraid, are fifty or sixty years old." To serve this kind of youth, Detroit cars have engines rated as high as 425 h.p., providing a vanity cushion of at least 250 h.p. beyond any practical day-to-day requirements of the vehicle. Along with this yearning for power—and as part of it—most drivers want to get some pleasure from the performance of their vehicles and engines. In fact, they may drive a car for that reason alone. "To drive a really fine, balanced car", says a road-racing champion, is "the most splendid and most rewarding . . . pleasure . . . known to man."

Dealing with pure function

The demands on a lorry are something else again, for a goods vehicle operates in an aura wholly different from that of a car. "Nobody wants a lorry for itself because they love a lorry," says an engineer who supervises the building of more lorries than any other person on earth. "They want a tool, and that's what a lorry is, a tool. The questions are: What are you going to use it for? What are you going to carry? How far? Over what kind of terrain? A big semi-trailer hauls loads of 73,000 pounds over smooth highways for distances of 2,000 miles and more. An earth-mover may haul twice that weight up gradients steeper than 30 per cent. And a medium lorry generally carries 10 tons of cargo on short hauls around a city. Whatever the lorry's purpose, its engine has very little surplus power built in: the medium lorry's engine turns out no more than 175 h.p. at a top r.p.m. of 3,400; the over-the-road semi-trailer perhaps 260 h.p. at 2,300 r.p.m. There is no vanity cushion for jack-rabbiting away from stop-lights or passing in tight places. "You're dealing in a lorry with pure function," says one lorry builder, "to get the load from here to there."

All these sharply differing demands—efficient hauling, comfortable travel, exhilarating speed—are met, in most American vehicles, by a remarkable complex of machinery: a four-cycle internal-combustion engine with gears to transmit power to the wheels and an electric motor to get the whole thing started. The basic design of the engine itself had changed very little since Nikolaus Otto developed it in Germany in 1876. In 1954 the rotary, or Wankel, engine was invented. It became increasingly popular during the 1970's because of its promise of remedying the problems of rising fuel costs and pollution. But the conventional piston engine still dominates the car market. The gears that actually move the wheels can be traced back through steam carriages to ancient clockwork. The one crucial innovation which made the motor vehicle convenient to use—and thus enabled horsepower to replace horses—was the starting mechanism, the most intricate, sensitive, and in many ways the most fascinating part of the entire vehicle.

A 20,000-volt spark

The moment the driver turns the key, he feeds an electric current from a storage battery to a small electric motor, which sets the engine turning over slowly. At the same time he completes the engine's ignition circuit. This is an electrical system connecting the battery to a set of voltage-transforming coils, then to a fast-acting switch, then through the sparking-plugs and finally back to the battery. The switch—a set of contacts called breaker points—opens and closes the circuit. As the current pulses go through the primary coil they generate a similarly pulsing field of magnetic force around the primary and therefore also around the concentric secondary coil. This causes a new current to flow in the secondary, since a changing magnetic field always induces electricity in a wire near it. But the secondary coil contains far more wire than the primary and as a result the voltage of the secondary current is proportionately increased. The 12 volts that the primary gets from the battery are stepped up to a powerful pulse of 20,000 volts, strong enough to create a spark inside the engine. The hot spark, arcing .035 inch between nickel-chrome electrodes at the base of the sparking plug, ignites a mixture of air and petrol vapour, and the expansive force of these burning gases provides the energy that moves the car.

Within the engine the sequence of operations leading to this power-producing ignition of gases involves four distinct cycles, or piston strokes. All four cycles follow in a specific order in each cylinder, whether the engine has six cylinders, like most lorries, or eight, like most passenger

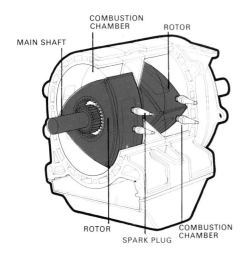

THE ROTARY, OR WANKEL, ENGINE has only two major moving parts, the rotor and the main shaft (*blue*). The triangular rotor with convex sides revolves in a combustion chamber shaped like a slightly pinched oval. The rotor apexes, which touch the inner surface of the combustion chamber, form three spaces between the wall and the rotor sides. As the rotor turns in a single revolution, the spaces change in size, allowing first the entry of the fuel-air mixture, then a sequence of compression and ignition, and finally exhaust. The power of a rotary engine increases by the addition of combustion chambers and rotors just as the addition of cylinders increases the horsepower of a piston-powered engine.

cars. The sequence of cycles begins as the electric starter motor cranks the engine. On stroke one, a piston moves to the bottom of the cylinder, creating a vacuum which sucks in the vaporized fuel mixture from the carburettor. On stroke two, the close-fitting piston is pushed back to the top of the cylinder, compressing the mixture. When the piston nears the top of the compression stroke, a carefully timed spark ignites the fuel. As the hot gases expand violently, the piston pushes downwards in the third, or power, stroke. On the fourth stroke, the piston returns to the top of the cylinder, forcing out the burnt gases through an exhaust valve, at the same time returning to the first position for the beginning of a new four-stroke cycle.

In the course of making this four-stroke cycle, the engine converts more than 25 per cent of the heat energy from the gases into work—over three times the thermal efficiency of the steam-engine. The key to such efficiency is the compression stroke, during which the piston squeezes down the fuel mixture to about one-ninth its original volume. The act of compression raises the temperature of the air-gas vapour mixture to nearly 400°C. before firing, providing that much of a head start towards ignition and towards the ultimate expansive force of the power stroke. Just after firing, the pressure of the expanding gases inside the cylinders is nearly 70 times as great as the pressure of the atmosphere.

The higher the initial pressure (and temperature), the more efficient the engine, since less fuel is used heating the mixture inside the cylinder to the flash point. In fact, if the pressure is great enough—about 600 pounds per square inch, giving a temperature of 540°C.—the fuel will ignite without any electric spark. This is the operating principle of the diesel engine, which will move a heavy vehicle while using 25 per cent less fuel than the same lorry would burn with a petrol engine.

A change in direction

After the fuel in a cylinder fires, the downward push of the piston is transmitted through a connecting rod to a crankshaft, which changes the up-and-down movement of the piston into rotating movement and thus into torque. There is some roughness in the rotating movement because of the quick, hard push of the piston, but this is smoothed out by a 30-pound cast-iron flywheel attached to the rear end of the crankshaft. In the petrol-burning sedan pick-up, the torque which the engine can ultimately supply to the driving wheels is 190 pounds-feet—plenty to move the unloaded vehicle on a flat road, but not close to the 1,650 pounds-feet needed to pull it up a 30 per cent gradient.

This discrepancy between the initial net torque and the full amount of torque required cannot be overcome by the engine itself. For while internal-combustion engines can vary the rate at which they produce

THE IGNITION SYSTEM, which makes an engine work by controlling the explosions in its cylinders, goes into operation when the ignition key is switched on. It opens a path for current (*medium grey*) from the battery to the distributor (*blue*). The cam repeatedly starts and stops the current, which activates a switch (*light grey*). This pulsing low-voltage current causes the coil to generate jolts of high-voltage current, which moves along a new circuit (*dark grey*) to the rotor. Each time the rotor passes one of the electrodes, it directs a burst of current to a sparking-plug, where electricity ignites gas to power the engine, releasing voltage, and flowing back to the battery via the return circuit (*light grey*).

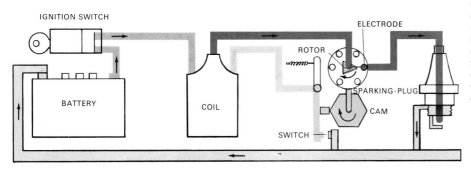

IGNITION SWITCH

ELECTRODE

ROTOR

SPARKING-PLUG

BATTERY

COIL

CAM

SWITCH

effort, they cannot—of themselves—effectively change the amount of effort they produce. The job of adjusting torque to suit the load and highway must be handled by a separate mechanism.

This is what the transmission, or gear-box, is for. "The engine's job", says one of the nation's leading lorry engineers, "is to provide enough torque to move the vehicle under its designed conditions. And if the initial torque is not adequate, you need to find some way to increase it."

Gears for greater power

The transmission accomplishes this increase through a system of gears, interposed between the engine and the driving wheels. One of these gears, which can be connected to or disconnected from the engine fly-wheel by a clutch (manual or automatic), brings engine torque into the transmission on a rotating input shaft. A simple manual gear-box, such as the sedan pick-up might have, contains this transmission input shaft gear plus a set of other gears of different sizes. Low gear is the equivalent of 2.79 times the diameter of the shaft gear; second gear is 1.70 times the equivalent diameter; and high is the same as the shaft gear. By moving his gear-shift lever to low, the driver engages the low-gear mechanism with the swiftly rotating shaft gear. Because the low gear has a size ratio of 2.79 to the shaft gear, it delivers 2.79 times as much torque. And because of its greater effective number of meshing teeth, it turns more slowly—one rotation for every 2.79 turns of the engine.

Torque gets an extra boost at the rear axle from an assembly called the differential. Here another set of gears automatically changes the direction of the rotational force from longitudinal to transverse. At the same time these differential gears hike the torque output by a factor of 3.25, for a total torque of 1,720 pounds-feet. Now the vehicle can make it up almost any slope.

But if the vehicle is a farmer's lorry or a 100-ton earth-mover, it must be ready to handle not only the steepest city streets but also the dizzying ramps in a gravel pit, a strip mine or a river embankment. Therefore, the farmer's lorry may have a low gear that multiplies the engine's effort six and a half times—compared to the sedan pick-up's 2.79. And a big gravel lorry's complex 16-position gear train can multiply the engine's gross torque of 840 pounds-feet by as much as 100 times before it reaches the driving wheels.

Besides its great power and versatility, the motor vehicle is a remarkably durable mechanism. The engine of the average car, driven with normal restraint, can go more than 50,000 miles before it needs major repairs. The modern lorry is even tougher: the owner of any inter-city fleet of tractor-trailers demands that every one of his vehicles be able to travel 300,000 miles in about two years before he has to take it in for a complete overhaul. However, there is nothing indestructible about the complex mechanism of a motor vehicle: each year in the U.S. garage service lorries respond to 70 million road calls to repair breakdowns, over one-quarter of them in the vehicles' sensitive electrical systems. Never-

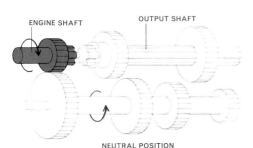

ENGINE SHAFT   OUTPUT SHAFT

NEUTRAL POSITION

A MANUAL TRANSMISSION for a car is shown on these pages in neutral and in three forward gear positions, providing successive combinations of speed and driving effort, or torque. In each diagram, engine power (*blue*) moves from left to right towards the wheels. In neutral (*above*) the transmission sends no power to the wheels because the engine and output shafts are not connected. Below, the driver has shifted to first gear, forcing the large gear (A) on the output shaft to move to the left (*arrow*), so that it engages a smaller gear (B) on the engine shaft by means of the cluster gear. This combination, by twice channelling the engine's power from smaller gears to larger ones, delivers maximum torque and low speed to start the wheels rolling.

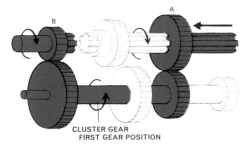

CLUSTER GEAR
FIRST GEAR POSITION

theless, the entire mechanism of the motor-car has progressed a long way since the pre-World War I days when a wise motorist carried a tool kit with 30 spare parts and 32 tools, and a Tin Pan Alley satirist produced a theme song for the amateur repairman entitled *Get Out and Get Under*.

As the motor vehicle developed its present durability, it also became the most useful—and the most used—piece of heavy machinery in the history of the world. Since the turn of the century, more than 300 million cars, lorries and buses have come out of U.S. factories; the rest of the world has produced about two-fifths that number. Today the motor vehicles of America annually travel the equivalent of five million trips to the moon. In the course of their travels they make more money and create more business than any other instrument of man's invention: one U.S. business in five is directly connected to the motor-vehicle industry, and £80,000 million a year goes into highway transportation. More than 12 cents out of every dollar spent by the U.S. wage earner is invested in his car. He also gives 13 per cent of the floor space in the house to keep the rain off his car. This nation's commitment to the motor vehicle is so complete that the Canadian philosopher Marshall McLuhan—among others—has described the U.S. as "an automobile culture". And on a more prosaic level, a Scandinavian military observer on the Korean front in the early 1950's noted that Americans seemed to have forgotten how to walk; anywhere we could build a road to bring in our equipment and troops, we were likely to win. But if a battle turned into a walking match over difficult terrain, we were in trouble. In 1980, our troops may be even less adaptable to marching. By that date U.S. soldiers will have grown up in a nation possessing three cars for every five citizens.

Mobility unlimited

The most striking aspect of this automobile culture is almost unlimited personal mobility; and this mobility has changed the country into a single, homogeneous community, a vast suburb paved with concrete. Near the end of the 19th century, nearly two-thirds of the U.S. lived on farms and in rural communities. There were very few suburbs. The radius of the average city was limited to about five miles from its rail terminals and port facilities. Factories were in the heart of town, and with few exceptions, people who worked in them lived in town. Today, with 80 per cent of the commuting labour force and 40 per cent or so of all the nation's freight tonnage moving by the grace of the internal-combustion engine, the radius of the city has spread to 40 miles.

In places like Detroit, Pittsburgh and Chicago, more people live on the fringes of the cities than in the business sections. Many of them no longer bother to go to the city centre at all. They find no reason to. In 1928 a group of businessmen in Ardmore, Pennsylvania, bought up a 20-acre estate on which they built the first complete shopping complex outside a major city. They called it Suburban Square, and it contained two major department stores, a bank, a bakery, a hardware store, an embryo supermarket, doctors' surgeries, a cinema, three clothing stores, a

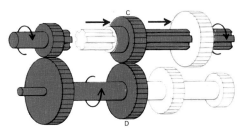

SECOND GEAR POSITION

HIGH GEAR SETTINGS accelerate the car and maintain cruising speed. In the diagram above, showing the second gear position, the output shaft gears have slid to the right, bringing into mesh a different pair of gears (C and D). This combination transmits medium speed and medium torque to the wheels so that the car can get up to its cruising speed. In the diagram below, of third, or high gear, position, the smaller output-shaft gear (C) has slid to the left, its collar locking the engine and output shafts together—and thus the engine's high speed and low torque are transmitted to the wheels for fast cruising. Some lorries have elaborate transmissions with 16 gear positions to use the engine's power most efficiently under all conditions.

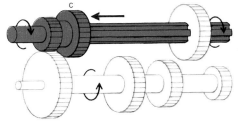

THIRD GEAR POSITION

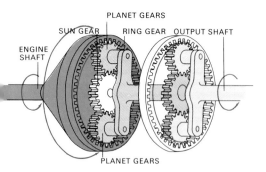

PLANETARY GEARS went out with the Model T but returned with automatic transmissions, which need gears that can be shifted while remaining interlocked. In the shifting process—governed by both acceleration pedal and wheel speed—one or more gears is stopped (*white*), altering the path of power through the moving gears (*blue*) to the output shaft connected to the wheels. In first gear position (*above*), the engine shaft turns the left ring which turns its planets around their stopped sun; this causes the right sun to rotate its planets within their stopped ring. This sends minimum speed and maximum torque to the output shaft, as indicated by shades of blue, which are lighter for lower speeds and higher torques. In second gear (*below*), the left ring gear is locked to its planets so that they and their sun turn as a unit. The right ring is stopped; thus its turning sun causes the planets to move round, turning the output shaft at moderate speed with about 60 per cent of maximum torque.

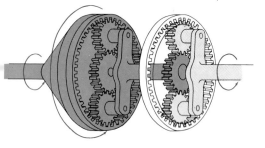

bookshop, record shop and a dozen other stores. Since then the suburban shopping centre has become a national institution, so completely car-orientated that it includes such facilities as drive-in banks, drive-in cinemas, drive-in restaurants—and, sometimes, motels.

Factories, too, have moved out of the city centre, relying on lorries to bring in raw materials and take out finished goods. In Detroit, for example, most car factories are in the suburbs; one assembly plant keeps 40 per cent of its inventory of parts rolling towards it over the highway, with only three days' supply stacked up at the plant itself. Other industries in other cities have followed suit. Houston, Los Angeles, San Francisco, Denver and Philadelphia have experienced a similar blossoming of suburban and ex-urban factories.

Outside the city, the motor vehicle has brought changes just as profound. In 1890 there were 4,600,000 million farms in the U.S. and 43 per cent of the entire U.S. work force laboured at farming. The average rural family, dependent on horses for personal transportation, rarely travelled more than 15 miles from its homestead in the course of a year—sometimes in the course of an entire lifetime. The farmer's wife shopped out of a mail-order catalogue, or at a village general store. The market for the farmer's produce—if he was one of the fortunate ones who had enough land and hands to grow a surplus much beyond his own family's needs—was likely to be that same small village, where demand and prices were both low. At best, he lived near a railhead; but this still meant a slow haul by horse-drawn wagon to the rail depot, and when he got there he had to take what was offered—there was no other place to shop around. Partly for these reasons, the average farmer of that day produced only enough food and fibre for six people, including himself.

The transformed farm

Today, with his farm equipment mechanized and with a lorry to move himself and his produce, he turns out enough food and fibre for 37 people. And that is just the average. In Georgia, one poultry producer each year ships 45 million birds by lorry. And a single Florida dairy serves a population of two million, spread over a radius of 150 miles. Together with their equally mobile beef- and grain-growing brothers, they have turned the traditional family activity of farming into a thriving business. In 1970 the entire nation of 203 million people was fed by fewer than 3,000,000 farms. Moreover, thanks to the almost unlimited mobility, life on those farms is much like life anywhere else. The farmer's wife often drives 20, 40, even 100 miles to shop at a major urban centre. The farmer's children are well educated at large central schools made possible by cars and buses, which ferry pupils to classrooms as far as 30 miles from their homes.

Besides creating a new dimension in mobility and whole new patterns of living, the motor vehicle—particularly the lorry—has moved in next to the railway as a formidable instrument for the long-distance hauling of heavy freight. Eight per cent of the lorries now manufactured are heavy-duty rigs running along superhighways parallel to established railway lines. On average, in the U.S., lorries charge five times as much as the railways to haul freight. But with fast and flexible schedules and door-to-door service, lorries now haul a little over a fifth of the nation's overland freight.

Death on the roads

Not all the effects of the motor vehicle, however, have been so beneficial. In addition to consuming large amounts of fuel and polluting the atmosphere with their exhausts, cars are the fifth-ranking cause of death of all Americans, and the leading cause for persons between the ages of five and 25. Since 1900, more than 1.5 million people of all ages have been killed on the U.S. highways, and the toll from 1960 to 1966 was greater than the total of all GIs lost in World War II. Though the motor car is at the heart of the matter, it does not bear all the blame. In fact there is considerable evidence that the driver and the roadway cause more accidents than does the vehicle.

In a two-year study of single-car accidents carried out by the California Highway Patrol, 67 per cent of the drivers in fatal crashes were found to have been drinking heavily; traffic engineers have calculated that accident rates at intersections drop 50 to 80 per cent when stop-sign cross-roads are replaced by clover-leaf overpasses; and roadside collisions are reduced almost to zero when lamp posts, trees, abutments and the like are cleared away from the edges of the highway. Nevertheless the car itself is in some measure guilty. Faulty mechanical equipment causes some accidents. But far worse has been the lack of safety features which can help prevent injury or death when an accident does occur. To limit the car's lethal properties, federal law now requires that all cars sold in the U.S. be fitted with safety equipment which ranges from movable steering columns to dual braking systems and seat-top head-rests.

The problems caused by the motor vehicle go beyond highway safety, pollution and fuel consumption. While lorries and cars have built the vast, prosperous megalopolis, they have created at the same time such a snarl of traffic that the driving speed at the peak of the morning rush hour on a so-called expressway leading into a major city is about 13 m.p.h.—a little faster than the bullock cart of Sehora, but not much.

Like the railway, the motor vehicle has evolved as a separate piece of technology moving along its own set path, without regard either to other modes of transportation, or to the environment within which the vehicle itself is to operate. "There has been a great fragmentation of the whole system", says one very candid car manufacturer. "There has been this division between the people who supply cars and the people who supply the roads. The automobile people have always done what they wanted to do—or what they thought the customer wanted—in the way of building a car. And the highway people do what they want to do. And the communities do what they want to do. There is no co-ordination, but there will have to be some soon."

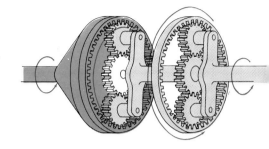

HIGHER GEAR POSITIONS in automatic transmissions furnish relatively light torque but send to the wheels speeds needed for driving on the road. For third gear position, shown above, the left sun gear is held stationary and the right planet gears are locked to their sun gear. The left ring turns its planets around their sun, producing more speed but less torque than second gear. This speed and torque are passed on to the output shaft unchanged by the right sun and planets, which turn with their ring as a unit. Fourth gear position (*below*) is obtained by locking the left planet gears on to their ring gear, and locking the right planet gears on to their sun gear. This causes all the gears in both left and right sets to turn as a unit, thus transmitting the speed and torque of the engine to the output shaft directly, without change. If all the gears in both sets were allowed to spin freely, the transmission would be in neutral, delivering no power to the output shaft.

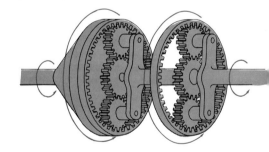

The Impact
of the Motor-Car

In 1900 the world had barely 10,000 motor-cars, and they were largely playthings for the rich. Seven decades later there were more than 230 million motor vehicles, and their effect on mankind is perhaps as great as that of any machine ever invented. They create jobs for some three million workers, consume materials drawn from all over the world and dispense products to every corner of Europe and the U.S.

Filling the demand for cars requires enough paper every year to print 31 million books, enough glass to provide windows for six million homes, enough steel to build 2,300 skyscrapers. Private expenditures on the motor-car make up nearly one-eighth of the average American's expenses; he spends almost as much on his car as he spends altogether on doctors, religion, charities, telephone, radio, television, furniture, electricity, petrol, books, magazines and newspapers.

So great is the economic impact of the motor vehicle today that its numbers often are used as a measure of a country's prosperity. In the United States, high sales of cars almost automatically mean a good year for all businesses. Elsewhere in the world, poor countries can be distinguished from the rich just by counting their cars and lorries.

HOW THE MOTOR-CAR MULTIPLIED
The fantastic numerical growth of the world's cars, lorries and buses is shown in this graph. Only 10,000 motor vehicles were registered in the world in 1900, but registrations rose sharply in the 1920's and by 1970 had soared over 230 million. The end of the car-population explosion is not in sight; by 1985 the number is expected to reach 360 million.

WORLD
MOTOR VEHICLE
REGISTRATIONS
(MILLIONS)

The Great and Odd Needs of Cars

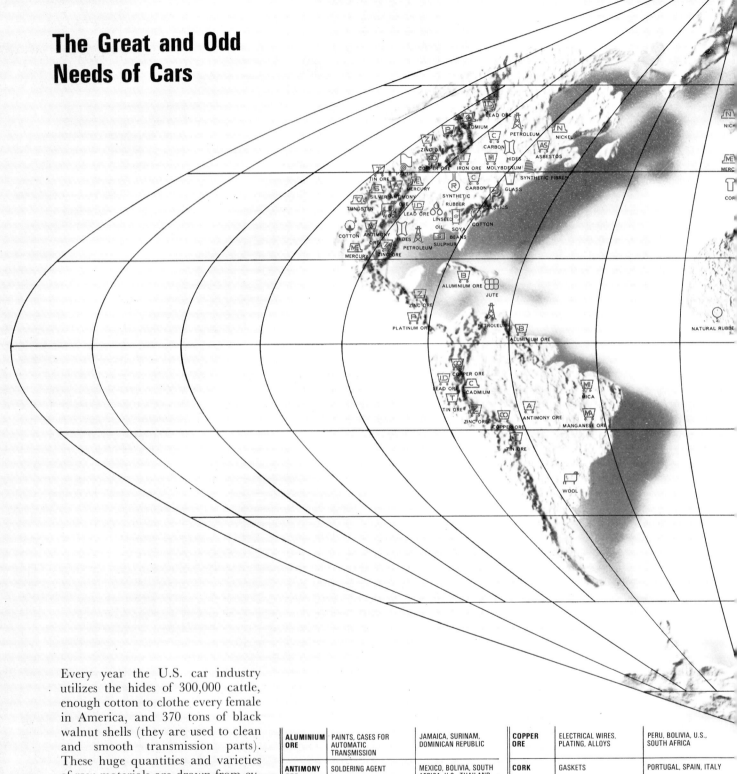

Every year the U.S. car industry utilizes the hides of 300,000 cattle, enough cotton to clothe every female in America, and 370 tons of black walnut shells (they are used to clean and smooth transmission parts). These huge quantities and varieties of raw materials are drawn from every part of the world, as is shown on this chart. Even remote Zambia, for example, supplies some of the asbestos for gaskets and brake linings.

Besides employing exotic products from faraway lands in commonplace ways, car manufacturers have found some exotic uses for everyday items. Margarine, for example, is used as a protective coating on car battery

ALUMINIUM ORE	PAINTS, CASES FOR AUTOMATIC TRANSMISSION	JAMAICA, SURINAM, DOMINICAN REPUBLIC	COPPER ORE	ELECTRICAL WIRES, PLATING, ALLOYS	PERU, BOLIVIA, U.S., SOUTH AFRICA
ANTIMONY ORE	SOLDERING AGENT	MEXICO, BOLIVIA, SOUTH AFRICA, U.S., THAILAND	CORK	GASKETS	PORTUGAL, SPAIN, ITALY
ASBESTOS	BRAKE LININGS, GASKETS, CLUTCH FACINGS	CANADA, SOUTH AFRICA, ZAMBIA	COTTON	PADDING, INSULATION, THREAD	EGYPT, INDIA, U.S., MEXICO
CADMIUM	PLATING FOR FASTENERS	CANADA, ZAIRE, PERU, JAPAN, AUSTRALIA	GLASS	WINDOWS	U.S.
CARBON	STEEL, RUBBER, GRAPHITE SEALS	CANADA, U.S.	HIDES	LEATHER UPHOLSTERY	CANADA, U.S.
CHROMIUM ORE	CHROME PLATING	PHILIPPINES, TURKEY, SOUTH AFRICA, ZAMBIA, MALAWI, U.S.S.R.	IRON ORE	STEEL AND CAST IRON	U.S.

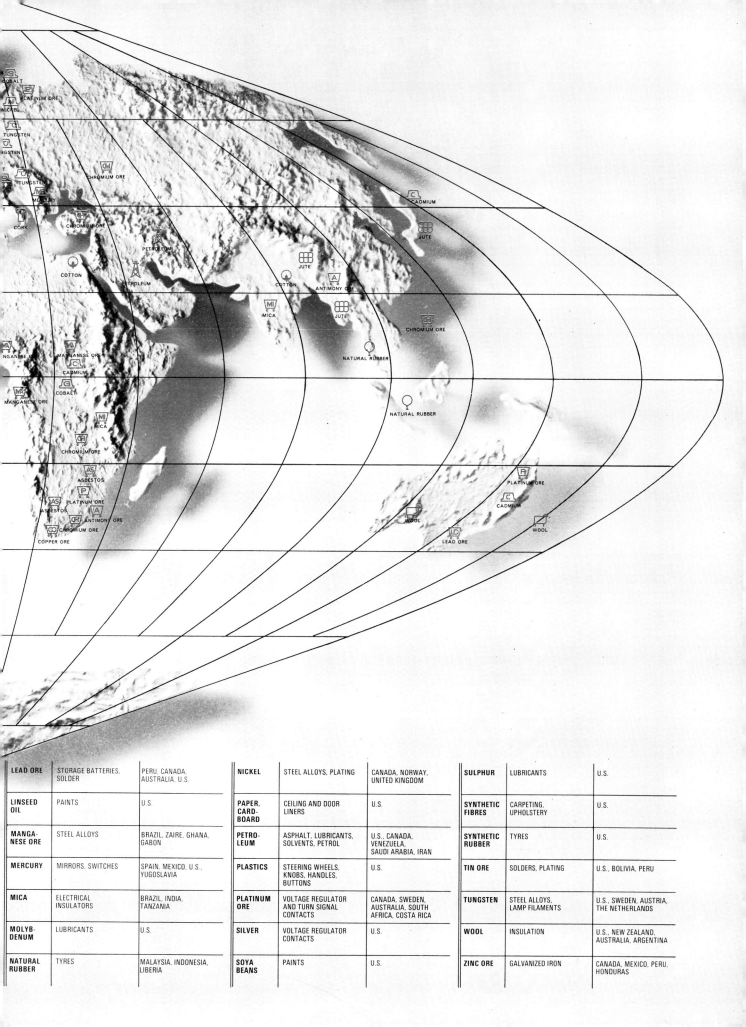

LEAD ORE	STORAGE BATTERIES, SOLDER	PERU, CANADA, AUSTRALIA, U.S.	NICKEL	STEEL ALLOYS, PLATING	CANADA, NORWAY, UNITED KINGDOM	SULPHUR	LUBRICANTS	U.S.
LINSEED OIL	PAINTS	U.S.	PAPER, CARDBOARD	CEILING AND DOOR LINERS	U.S.	SYNTHETIC FIBRES	CARPETING, UPHOLSTERY	U.S.
MANGANESE ORE	STEEL ALLOYS	BRAZIL, ZAIRE, GHANA, GABON	PETROLEUM	ASPHALT, LUBRICANTS, SOLVENTS, PETROL	U.S., CANADA, VENEZUELA, SAUDI ARABIA, IRAN	SYNTHETIC RUBBER	TYRES	U.S.
MERCURY	MIRRORS, SWITCHES	SPAIN, MEXICO, U.S., YUGOSLAVIA	PLASTICS	STEERING WHEELS, KNOBS, HANDLES, BUTTONS	U.S.	TIN ORE	SOLDERS, PLATING	U.S., BOLIVIA, PERU
MICA	ELECTRICAL INSULATORS	BRAZIL, INDIA, TANZANIA	PLATINUM ORE	VOLTAGE REGULATOR AND TURN SIGNAL CONTACTS	CANADA, SWEDEN, AUSTRALIA, SOUTH AFRICA, COSTA RICA	TUNGSTEN	STEEL ALLOYS, LAMP FILAMENTS	U.S., SWEDEN, AUSTRIA, THE NETHERLANDS
MOLYBDENUM	LUBRICANTS	U.S.	SILVER	VOLTAGE REGULATOR CONTACTS	U.S.	WOOL	INSULATION	U.S., NEW ZEALAND, AUSTRALIA, ARGENTINA
NATURAL RUBBER	TYRES	MALAYSIA, INDONESIA, LIBERIA	SOYA BEANS	PAINTS	U.S.	ZINC ORE	GALVANIZED IRON	CANADA, MEXICO, PERU, HONDURAS

Two Nations:
The Effect on Prosperity

SPAIN	1965
WEST GERMANY	1965

Spain has twice the area and half the population of West Germany, yet it produces goods and services worth only one-fifth as much. The difference can be measured by the car, which is both a cause and an effect of each country's national wealth.

West Germany (*opposite*), its efficient industries aided by the huge numbers of cars and lorries used at home and exported abroad, enjoys the high incomes, educational level and service industries that go with advanced technology. The economy of

Spain, by contrast, is relatively backward. Although the nation is making progress in manufacturing—it turned out more than 400,000 motor vehicles in 1966 and is enduring mounting traffic jams as one result of its new affluence—it is still known more for its famous sherry and bullfighters (*above*) than for its industry. One revealing statistic concerns farm tractors: Spain, though an agricultural nation, has only 13 tractors for every 10,000 acres of farmland; West Germany, an industrial nation, has 284.

195,000

95,700

59,000,000

112

1,440

31,600,000

593

19.1

AREA
(SQUARE MILES)

POPULATION

GROSS NATIONAL
PRODUCT
$1,000,000,000

INCOME PER
CAPITA
(DOLLARS)

AUTOMOTIVE WORKERS	CARS PER 10,000 POPULATION	LORRIES PER 10,000 POPULATION	PASSENGER CARS MANUFACTURED	COMMERCIAL VEHICLES MANUFACTURED	PASSENGER CARS	PASSENGER CARS	AVERAGE PURCHASE PRICE	HIGHWAY EXPENDITURES (DOLLARS)	MADE-UP ROADS	PERCENTAGE OF WORKERS IN AGRICULTURE	TRACTORS PER 10,000 ACRES
491,000	1,700	116	2,730,000	230,000	279,000	1,520,000	2,510	1,750	150,000	30.7	284
40,700	255	161	146,000	83,200	8,560	1,430		5.20	27,000	10.9	13
								21.9			

How the Car
Remade America

In a half century, the car has changed the United States as dramatically as the car itself has been transformed (*chart on the right*). In 1920, the heyday of the Model T Ford (*above*), 83 per cent of all cars produced were canvas-topped and their tyres lasted only 5,000 miles. Half the population then lived in the country and children trudged to one-teacher schools.

By 1970, Ford's standard-sized car was large and sleek (*right*). Urban population had soared, travel had increased, farm horses were rare, and one-teacher schools had given way to regional schools served by buses.

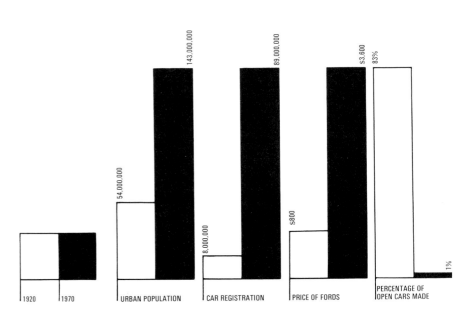

1920 · 1970 · URBAN POPULATION · 54,000,000 · 143,000,000 · CAR REGISTRATION · 8,000,000 · 89,000,000 · PRICE OF FORDS · $800 · $3,600 · PERCENTAGE OF OPEN CARS MADE · 83% · 1%

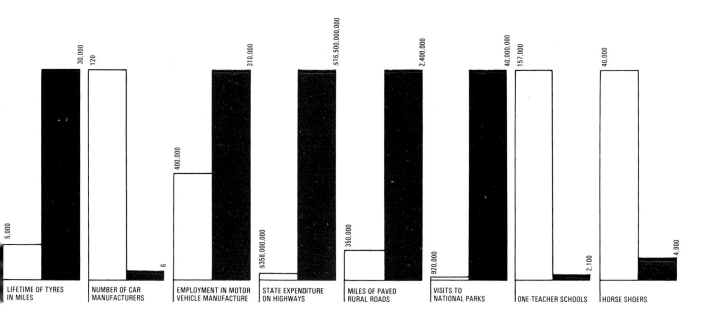

30,000	120		310,000	$16,500,000,000	2,400,000	40,000,000	157,000	40,000
		400,000						
5,000					350,000			
			$358,000,000		920,000		2,100	4,000
	6							
LIFETIME OF TYRES IN MILES	NUMBER OF CAR MANUFACTURERS	EMPLOYMENT IN MOTOR VEHICLE MANUFACTURE	STATE EXPENDITURE ON HIGHWAYS	MILES OF PAVED RURAL ROADS	VISITS TO NATIONAL PARKS		ONE-TEACHER SCHOOLS	HORSE SHOERS

An Economy on Wheels

The motor-car is so vitally involved in every aspect of the American economy that one U.S. business in five is directly connected with it in some way. There are now about 30,000 new-car dealers, 100,000 repair garages and 3,500 car manufacturers. One manufacturer, General Motors, is the world's eighth largest corporation (the largest, the American Telephone and Telegraph Company, owns the world's biggest private fleet of motor vehicles). There are also armoured car services and oil refineries, one-minute car washes and taxi companies, motels and paint shops, all owing their existence to the motor-car. Their gross incomes total £90,000 million every year. And they generate more than 12 million jobs, employing one-sixth of all the country's workers.

The breadth and depth of the car's impact are shown graphically in these charts of five sectors of the U.S. economy. In each panel the upper chart contrasts the 1970 automotive figures (blue) with other important figures in the same economic sector; each of the lower charts shows subdivisions of the automotive data.

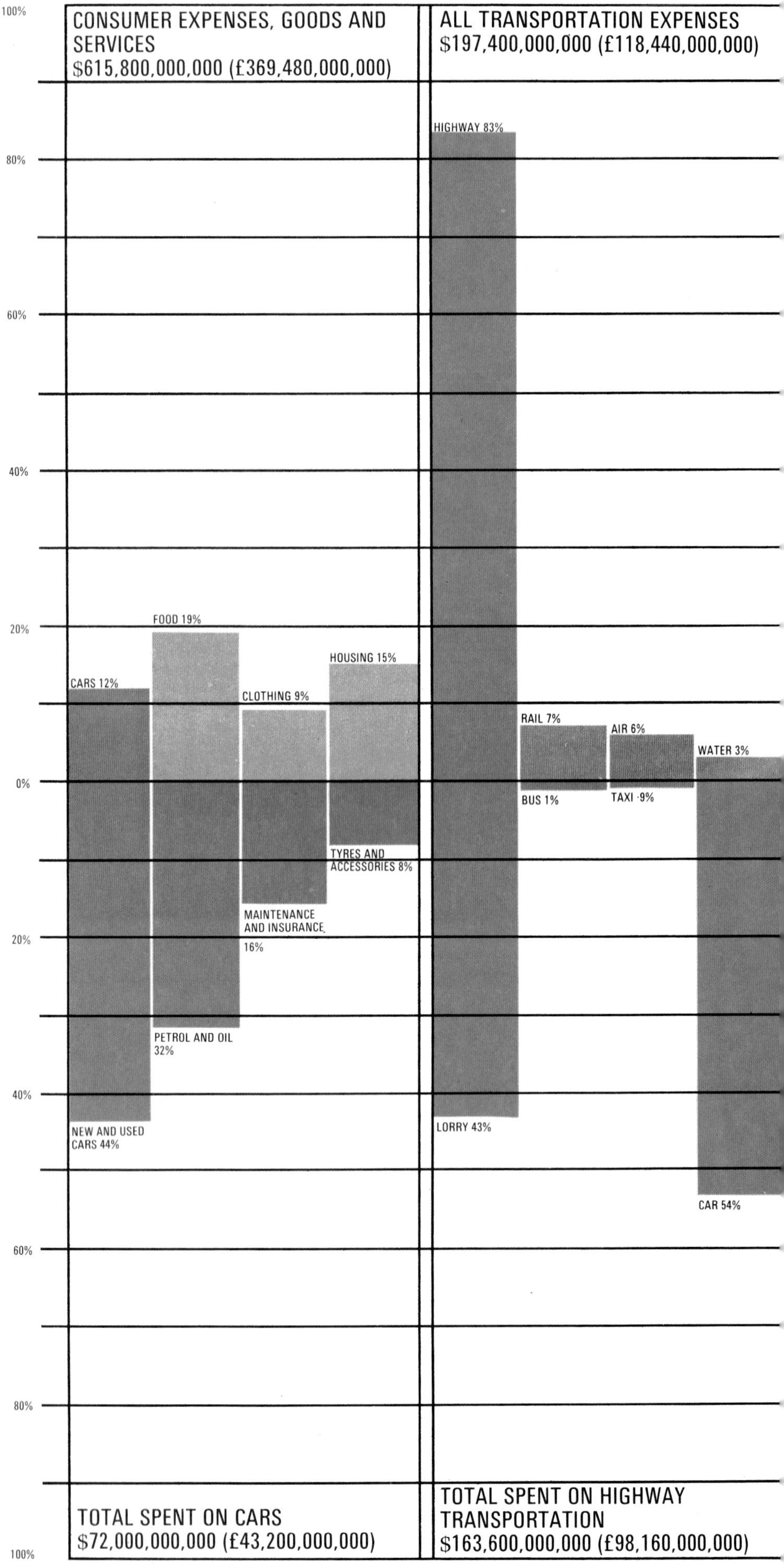

CONSUMER EXPENSES, GOODS AND SERVICES $615,800,000,000 (£369,480,000,000)

ALL TRANSPORTATION EXPENSES $197,400,000,000 (£118,440,000,000)

HIGHWAY 83%

FOOD 19%

HOUSING 15%

CARS 12%

CLOTHING 9%

RAIL 7%

AIR 6%

WATER 3%

BUS 1%

TAXI 9%

TYRES AND ACCESSORIES 8%

MAINTENANCE AND INSURANCE 16%

PETROL AND OIL 32%

NEW AND USED CARS 44%

LORRY 43%

CAR 54%

TOTAL SPENT ON CARS $72,000,000,000 (£43,200,000,000)

TOTAL SPENT ON HIGHWAY TRANSPORTATION $163,600,000,000 (£98,160,000,000)

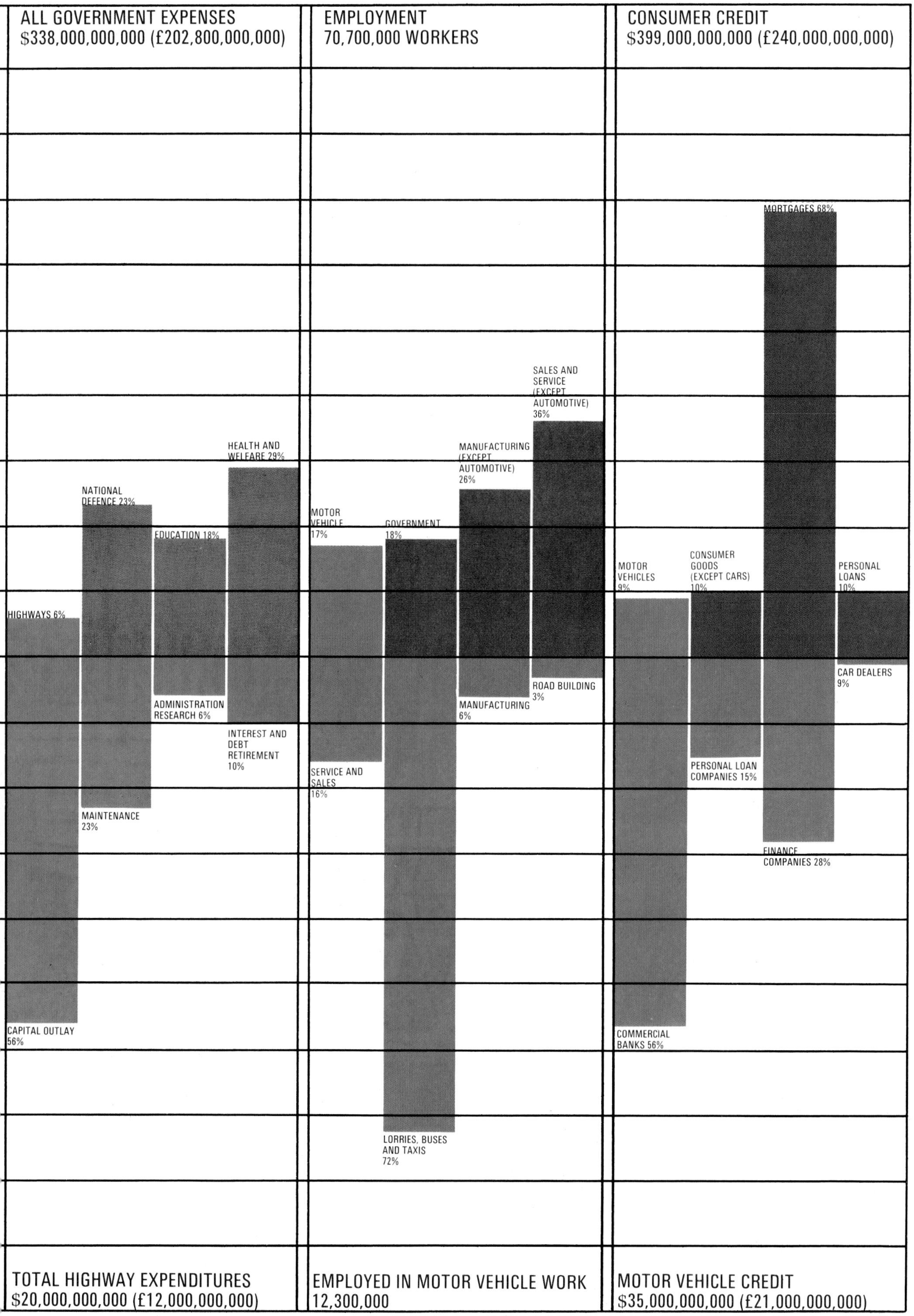

ALL GOVERNMENT EXPENSES $338,000,000,000 (£202,800,000,000)	EMPLOYMENT 70,700,000 WORKERS	CONSUMER CREDIT $399,000,000,000 (£240,000,000,000)

MORTGAGES 68%

SALES AND SERVICE (EXCEPT AUTOMOTIVE) 36%

HEALTH AND WELFARE 29%

MANUFACTURING (EXCEPT AUTOMOTIVE) 26%

NATIONAL DEFENCE 23%

EDUCATION 18%

MOTOR VEHICLE 17%

GOVERNMENT 18%

CONSUMER GOODS (EXCEPT CARS) 10%

MOTOR VEHICLES 9%

PERSONAL LOANS 10%

HIGHWAYS 6%

CAR DEALERS 9%

ADMINISTRATION RESEARCH 6%

ROAD BUILDING 3%

MANUFACTURING 6%

INTEREST AND DEBT RETIREMENT 10%

PERSONAL LOAN COMPANIES 15%

SERVICE AND SALES 16%

MAINTENANCE 23%

FINANCE COMPANIES 28%

CAPITAL OUTLAY 56%

COMMERCIAL BANKS 56%

LORRIES, BUSES AND TAXIS 72%

TOTAL HIGHWAY EXPENDITURES $20,000,000,000 (£12,000,000,000)	EMPLOYED IN MOTOR VEHICLE WORK 12,300,000	MOTOR VEHICLE CREDIT $35,000,000,000 (£21,000,000,000)

A 7,141-Mile Hamburger

Before the hamburger and milk shake on the right could be served at a Woodbridge drive-in restaurant off the New Jersey Turnpike, some 30 separate lorry trips totalling 7,141 miles had to be made to assemble the various ingredients. The details, provided in the chart below, show how completely lorries have taken over farm-to-consumer food shipments. Today, all of America's eggs and poultry, all of its hogs and about 98 per cent of its cattle go to market by lorry. Farmers and food shippers operate some 3.8 million lorries, over 20 per cent of the national total.

The lorries that carry food are familiar types. But special vehicles have also been designed for almost every imaginable purpose. One type carries 200-ton loads of logs from forest to mill; another carries complete houses from old sites to new ones; still another hauls 65,000 live trout at a time from hatcheries to streams 500 miles away. There are bookmobiles, bloodmobiles, travelling museums and, in some communities, even mobile swimming pools on lorries.

ITEM AND SOURCE		LORRY-MILES
PLASTIC SPOON, FROM WILMINGTON, MASS.		360
PAPER NAPKINS, FROM WISCONSIN		1,350
MILK SHAKE	SUGAR, FROM NEW ORLEANS, 1,350 MILES IMPORTED FLAVOURING FROM NEW YORK, 20 MILES MILK FROM PERTH AMBOY, 2 MILES	1,372
PICKLES, FROM REVERE, MASS.		250
BEEF, FROM KANSAS CITY		1,350
ROLL	FLOUR, FROM NEBRASKA, 1,544 MILES BAKED ROLL, FROM QUINCY, MASS., 235 MILES	1,779
ONIONS, FROM ROCHESTER, N.Y.		405
SALT, FROM SYRACUSE, N.Y.		275
TOTAL LORRY-MILES		**7,141**

10,000 Miles at Seven Pence a Mile

The legendary little old lady who drives her car only on Sunday may think she is being economical; the fact is, she is something of a spendthrift. Her weekly trip to church may cost her as much as 52p a mile—about seven times what she would pay per mile if she drove as the average motorist does, 10,000 miles a year.

As the chart on the right shows, the big expense of a car is not in driving it but owning it. The cost of running a car 10,000 miles annually, when averaged over its normal lifetime of 10 years, is about 7p a mile. Almost half of that sum, or 3½p, is in fixed costs, which tend to remain the same whether the car is carefully wrapped in a plastic sheet in the garage or is out rolling along a highway. Even depreciation—the cost of amortizing the original purchase price of the car—changes only slightly with use. The only thing the little old lady really saves is wear and tear on her nerves—and not much of that if she does all her driving in Sunday traffic.

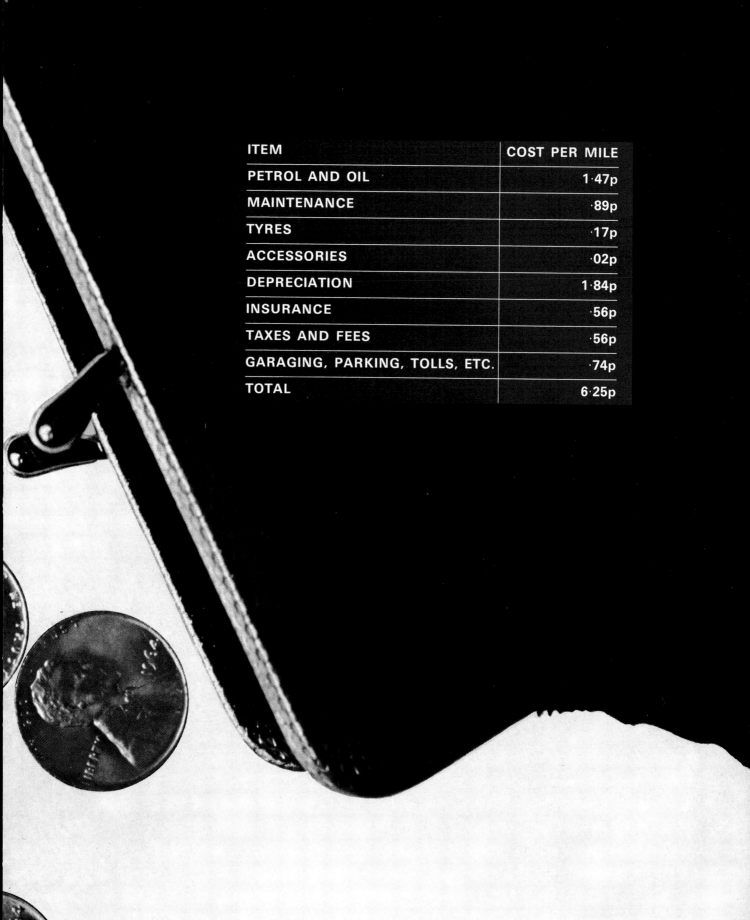

ITEM	COST PER MILE
PETROL AND OIL	1·47p
MAINTENANCE	·89p
TYRES	·17p
ACCESSORIES	·02p
DEPRECIATION	1·84p
INSURANCE	·56p
TAXES AND FEES	·56p
GARAGING, PARKING, TOLLS, ETC.	·74p
TOTAL	6·25p

5

Arteries
of
Civilization

Once nearly inaccessible, the natural beauties of the Blue Ridge mountains were brought within reach of motorists by this scenic parkway, opened in 1936. Running along forested peaks for 469 miles, it attracted over 14 million sightseers in 1973.

IN BRAZIL, a narrow smear of road cuts 1,340 miles through the central plateau from the river port of Belém to the capital city of Brasília. During the rainy season, the right-of-way disintegrates into a bog; in dry weather, it becomes an axle-bending torture track of sand and ruts. But these crude paths, hacked through scrub and jungle at a cost of £18 million, have been called the instrument for bringing a "new civilization on to the central plateau". In the first half-dozen years after the road was opened, some 700,000 new settlers flooded on to the plateau. Cattle herds multiplied to four million head, and beef began moving at a handsome profit by truck to markets in Brasília and Belém. A tumbledown railhead like Anápolis blossomed into a wide-awake city of 80,000, complete with four new 15-storey office buildings. And the countryside began girding for a wave of industrial development following the discovery off the highway of nickel, iron, copper, zinc, tin, lead and gold.

Nearly 5,000 miles away, the six lanes of Massachusetts Route 128, divided by a grassy median into a pair of swift-flowing streams of one-way traffic, carve a semicircle of fresh prosperity across the shoulder of Boston. When the road opened in 1952, the land on its flanks was a tired compost of chicken coops, bogs and tomato farms worth at most about £400 an acre. Thirteen years later, property adjacent to the highway was dotted with nearly 600 new firms, many of them devoted to Space-Age activities such as computer manufacture, optics and electronic research. These companies, whose products demanded the sort of gentle handling and close delivery schedules that highway carriers can provide, created 55,000 new jobs in exurban Boston—and boosted local land values to as high as £32,000 an acre.

Wherever and whenever a new road goes into a region, powerful forces of change come rolling down that right-of-way. For without a decent road, the finest wheel in the world has nowhere to roll. In underdeveloped countries, the mobility created by a new roadway releases the pent-up productivity of the land, and sets in motion a flow of goods, people and ideas. And as a nation begins to grow into the industrial world of the 20th century, it demands more sophisticated roadways to carry its commerce. For example, Russia (where about 50 per cent of inter-city passenger traffic and 65 per cent of all freight still move by rail) has been in the throes of a 10-year road-building programme to construct six- to eight-lane super-highways between Moscow and other major cities.

No such project approaches the gigantic, unending effort of the United States to provide adequate roadways for its flood of traffic. Every year America spends about £6,250 million to lay down or resurface 120,000 miles of highways and streets. The showiest part of this awe-inspiring programme is the 42,500-mile National System of Interstate and Defense Highways, every mile embodying advanced concepts which grew out of the pioneering Pennsylvania Turnpike. The steepest hill on the Interstate System rises about 5 feet in every 100. The sharpest curve on the wide-open right-of-way lets the driver see ahead a minimum of 1,200 feet—twice as far as he needs to stop at any speed up to 80 m.p.h. Cloverleaf interchanges eliminate the dangers and delays of highway cross-roads. A median divider, spreading in some places to as much as half a mile, minimizes the glare of headlights and virtually abolishes head-on collisions.

This sprawling web of highways represents the climax of almost 2,500 years of experimentation and progress in highway engineering. Its direct ancestor was the Roman road system, a superb network which totalled 53,658 miles of painstakingly paved and graded highways, including 29 magnificent military roads, every one of them measured from a golden milestone in the centre of the Roman Forum. These were the roads of Pompey, of Caesar and Augustus, laid down to permit armies to move quickly to any frontier for a fresh conquest, or to squash an incipient rebellion in the provinces. And once a new territory was completely in hand, the roads provided an artery of communication for the fast couriers who carried the messages of government.

A passion for order

Wherever the Roman roads reached out, their paths were as straight as a people with a passion for order could reasonably make them. Thanks to the mobility provided by these highways, Roman law, Roman peace, Roman goods and Roman ideas went out to the full breadth of the domain, which embraced 54 million people throughout virtually all the Western world.

When Rome fell, the mobility of the world fell with it. By 1571, on the road between Frankfurt and Marburg there was a hole so vast and deep that three carts plunged into it, and a peasant drowned in the muck at the bottom. The streets of Paris were a meandering swamp in which even royalty could come to grief: out riding one day, Prince Philip Augustus, son of Louis VII, was thrown into the goo when his horse shied at a pig—whereupon old Louis, no road engineer, ordered that all pigs be kept off the streets. But Philip, when he became king, promptly paved the road. Other kings in other countries took steps of their own to improve the flow of traffic. In Germany, a country road had to be wide enough "to let a man pass with a dead corpse on a cart". In town the houses had to be spaced to allow passage by a "knight in full armour carrying a spear crosswise". Despite these good intentions, highway engineering remained literally stuck in the mud until the end of the 18th century.

The man who did most to pull it out was an aristocratic Scotsman named John Loudon McAdam. Born near Glasgow in 1756, McAdam was chief supply agent for the British Navy on the west coast of England. Business was good, but it would have been even better had not the roads been in such a "wikkid" condition that wagon freight rates ran the costs of shipment much higher than a good Scotsman was willing to endure. For 15 years McAdam spent every spare moment studying the existing methods of road construction, and picking over the remains of the old Roman highways, with their massive stone surfaces and four-foot-deep subgrades. And whenever McAdam could get anyone

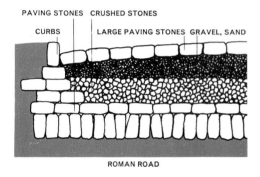

PAVING STONES   CRUSHED STONES

CURBS   LARGE PAVING STONES   GRAVEL, SAND

ROMAN ROAD

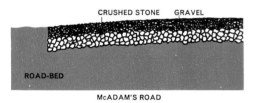

CRUSHED STONE   GRAVEL

ROAD-BED

McADAM'S ROAD

DURABLE ROADS were designed by the Romans and radically simplified in the early 19th century by the Scottish engineer John McAdam. The Romans laid down heavy foundations of two rows of stone blocks in clay or mortar, added layers of gravel and sand, and finally applied a paving of stones bound with mortar. McAdam's simpler method placed the weight of traffic directly on the road-bed; the bed was kept dry by covering it with one layer of gravel which was pounded down by traffic. Modern road builders use McAdam's method, but add top layers of concrete or asphalt to cover the gravel.

to listen, he talked about a newer, lighter, simpler road-building method.

McAdam kept insisting "that it is the native soil which really supports the weight of traffic; that while it is preserved in a dry state, it will carry any weight without sinking and that it does in fact carry the road and the carriages also". This notion clashed head on with the time-honoured Roman principle that only a stout sub-base of big stones could stand up to the pounding of heavy traffic. Just as radical was another of McAdam's ideas: the running surface of the road should be built primarily to keep the subsoil dry, and only secondarily to provide a smooth ride. "[The] native soil must be previously made quite dry," he insisted, "and a covering impenetrable to rain must then be placed over it in that dry state. ... The thickness of the road should only be regulated by the quantity of material necessary to form such impervious covering."

The power of persuasion

Having challenged the major precepts of conventional road building, McAdam cast around for a chance to prove he was right. He got that chance when he was appointed General Surveyor of the City of Bristol, and put in charge of the maintenance and rebuilding of 146 miles of wagon and State roads. Using a skeleton gang of no more than five men who carried only shovels, rakes, picks and one-pound hammers, McAdam gave each right-of-way a gentle crown of three or four inches. On either side of the road he dug drainage ditches. Then he spread his "impervious covering", which was nothing more than a 10-inch layer of crushed rock compacted under the weight of traffic.

McAdam's roads were cheap, easy and immensely successful. The native soil, protected by the layer of crushed rock, successfully supported "the weight of traffic"—just as it does today on all major road-beds, which are built according to McAdam's prescription improved only by the addition of a more impervious top surface and some extra layers of subbase to handle the heavier flow of vehicles.

McAdam's method quickly spread through Great Britain, and in 1825 a grateful government granted him a special award of £2,000. A year later, journalist Charles James Apperley testified, "I really consider Mr. McAdam as being [one of] the greatest contributors to the welfare of mankind that [his] country has ever produced".

So did the United States. In 1806 Congress had authorized a National Road to be laid through the mountains from Cumberland, Maryland, to Wheeling, West Virginia. And in 1825 Secretary of War Barbour announced, "After the most mature consideration, I have determined that [we shall complete the road] on the McAdam plan, the principles of which are simple, and have been tested by the experience of England".

Work crews laid a 30-foot McAdam strip in the crowned centre of the 68-foot right-of-way through the wilderness, and when they finished, a torrent of traffic began moving over it. A fast stage could now cover more than 200 miles in $23\frac{1}{2}$ hours. Better yet, the freight rate for carrying 100 pounds for 300 miles fell from 10 dollars to 3 dollars. Henry Clay, the

American politician, spoke rapturously of 80,000 miles of post road carrying "the wave of population, cultivation, and intelligence [to] the Pacific". But the time was not right. The excitement and energy of the U.S. was suddenly taken up by a different kind of road, the road for the iron horse, which pulled freight at less than half the old highway cost, and hauled passengers at nearly twice the speed of a fast stage-coach. In 1830, President Jackson vetoed federal aid for additional roads on rather foggy constitutional grounds; the Cumberland Road gradually sank into a state of disrepair, and the general science of highway engineering fell back into the morass where John McAdam had found it 50 years before.

The roadmakers' dark ages

The dark ages of road building lasted for nearly three-quarters of a century. In 1904, only 250 miles of U.S. roads outside the big cities had hard-top surfacing. And as late as 1914, the U.S. had no more than 10,500 miles of black-top highways and 2,348 in concrete. Of a short car trip through rural Minnesota during this period, Sinclair Lewis wrote: "The road ahead was a wet black smear, criss-crossed with ruts. The car shot into a morass of prairie gumbo—which is mud mixed with tar, fly-paper, fish, glue, and well-chewed chocolate-covered caramels. . . . When the wheels struck the slime, they slid, they wallowed. The car skidded . . . terrifyingly out of control".

At last, in the 1920's the technology of road building began to catch up with the technology of the motor vehicle. The U.S. government had just gone back into the road-building business with the Federal-Aid Road Act, which permitted the government to share with the States the planning and financing of highways. New specialists, the traffic and highway engineers, came on the scene to adapt the carriage roads of history to the demands of a mobile-minded population which by then owned some 15 million motor vehicles.

One way to make highways safer was to limit the number of side roads and cross-streets that cut into a major highway. Under the old common law, any property owner with land adjacent to a highway had "right of access" to the road. New York changed the law, and in November 1925 opened the Bronx River Parkway, a 15.5-mile section of a four-lane track interrupted by only three major level crossings (which were quickly removed). Better still, over three long stretches opposing traffic was divided into one-way streams by wide islands of grass and trees. Three years later in Woodbridge, New Jersey, the U.S. got its first cloverleaf interchange, a system of overpasses tied into swooping access lanes which allows traffic on two divided highways to cross and merge without inconvenient stops and with no danger of head-on collision.

Those innovations are merely the most obvious of the changes that highway engineers have introduced over the past decades. Now they also make their roads wider and smoother, with gentler curves and easier gradients. "We learned a lot of this from the railroad", said George Williams, an engineer who directed highway operations for the U.S. gov-

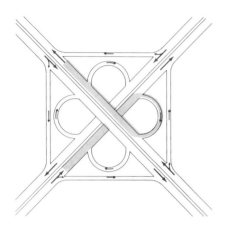

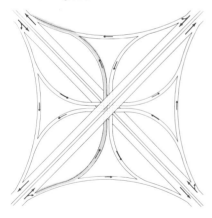

EXPRESSWAY INTERSECTIONS, the cloverleaf (*top*) and the directional interchange (*bottom*) provide access from one highway to another while eliminating the need for traffic to cross in front of oncoming vehicles. The cloverleaf is less expensive to build; the directional interchange is safer. On the cloverleaf a driver headed north-east who wants to go off to the north-west (*blue*) must first weave through the right lane's incoming traffic, which speeds up while he is slowing down. On the directional interchange he simply turns to the right without interference from incoming cars.

ernment for many years. "They laid out with the idea of the shortest, safest, most economical route per ton-mile. They could have only so much gradient, and so sharp a curve. You can't run a locomotive around a button-hook." Nor can you do so with a heavy lorry. A 36-ton semi-trailer booming along at 65 m.p.h. needs a curve with a minimum radius of 2,800 feet, banked at an angle of half an inch to every foot of road width. To hold to a minimum climbing speed of 20 m.p.h., these big lorries require gradients not much above 3 per cent.

The pioneer expressway

The first U.S. highway to try to answer these needs was the Pennsylvania Turnpike, which was laid down on the right-of-way constructed for the old South Penn Railroad. Opened in October 1940 along a 160-mile route between Harrisburg and Pittsburgh, the Turnpike bypassed all intermediate towns and limited access to cloverleaf interchanges. Its two broad ribbons of concrete were divided by a median strip. Every one of its curves was built to keep a runaway vehicle safely on the road at 90 m.p.h.; and no lorry or car had to climb a hill steeper than 3 feet in every 100 (some of the old roads near by were five times as steep).

Today, all these principles have been combined in the Interstate Highway System, planned to link together almost every U.S. city over 50,000 at a cost of £26,000 million. An astonishingly large part of this immense effort is expended well in advance of construction. Before the first bulldozer rumbles into action on a projected right-of-way for the system, a corps of mathematicians, economists, psychologists and traffic engineers collects data on the travel habits of people in the area through which the highway will go: How many cars and lorries roll over existing roadways? How often does each motorist use his vehicle? How far does he go? Which route does he take? These data are then analysed with the help of a computer to see how traffic on a theoretical highway would behave.

Once the traffic projections are in hand, the first tentative route for the highway is traced on U.S. Geological Survey terrain maps. Then a plane armed with a £8,000 camera of the type that pin-pointed German buzz-bomb sites in World War II skims over the general area of the right-of-way, taking thousands of overlapping pictures. The pictures are merged into a single, three-dimensional view of the terrain so clearly defined that photo-analysts can see the wires in a chicken coop and cartographers can plot elevations to an accuracy of a single foot.

The tentative route is then drawn on the photograph, and the men who lay it out must use all the mental agility of a backfield of broken-field runners. Ideally, the route should avoid cutting through towns, factories, rivers, housing developments, hospitals, railway tracks, lakes, swamps, reservoirs, tall hills and deep ravines. Practically, this is impossible. Wherever there is an unavoidable hill to be cut through, the road builders hope they will excavate exactly enough dirt and rock to fill a swamp or a ravine just up the road. Usually they do. When the proposed route hits a populated area, the planners may find themselves threading through a tangle of backyards and distraught landholders. Several times property adjusters for the New York State Thruway encountered local farmers literally in tears at being asked to move off the land where they had been born. At the town of Canajoharie the engineers discovered they had exactly 117 feet—the highway's prescribed minimum width—between the edge of the old New York State barge canal and the inviolable structure of a school. The most difficult obstacle of all can be a graveyard. "In New Rochelle," recalls Conrad Lang, formerly Chief Engineer of the New York State Thruway Authority, "the route went through an old Huguenot cemetery. It was like an archaeological exploration: every single bone had to be carefully and reverently removed, and then re-interred in a specially prepared site."

With the tentative route and the property claims settled, the chief engineer and his staff go out and walk the line, picking over every foot for final judgements on the path the highway will take. They may decide to put in a curve here, a bend there, even where there are no obstacles. "We find a little variety keeps the drivers awake", says one road architect. "Besides, wherever we can we try to adapt the highway to the land, get in some graceful contours instead of driving the road straight ahead the way they used to out west, and the way the Romans often did."

As they walk the line, the engineers follow every stream, each tiny dry gulch, to its source, study rainfall charts for the previous 50 years, and then calculate the sizes of culverts and bridges needed to keep flood water off the road. Soil samples go back to a laboratory, where tests indicate the ability of that soil to resist sliding, thus allowing the excavators to decide how steeply they can cut their embankments.

Finally, a survey party marks off the final line for each half of the divided highway. In some places the two halves will be divided by a mall only a few feet wide. In others, they are more than 2,000 feet apart, with differences in elevation of up to 100 feet.

A road-bed made with loving care

Then the earth-movers take over in gangs of more than 1,000 men. Their armoury of equipment includes scrapers able to scoop up 60 tons at one pass; mammoth off-highway lorries that muscle tons of fill up the steepest gradients; tractor-powered rippers whose steel teeth chew into solid rock in the way a dog goes through a turkey bone. After the basic path is hewn out, 10-ton rollers lovingly compact the top four feet of subgrade—layer by six-inch layer; the largest stone in the subgrade may be no bigger than a man's fist, and the final surface is as smooth as the aisle of a church.

Before the road surfacers move in, the road-bed gets one last, foot-thick layer of gravel, sometimes topped with a coating of the finest sand. When everything is ready, the 10-inch-thick reinforced concrete running surface is laid out like a carpet by massive, push-button-guided automatic pavers. In seven days the road is dry enough for a test car to drive on; in three weeks it can be opened to traffic.

And the traffic comes, in vast, unpredictable waves. Despite the electronic genius of the computer, traffic projections for a superhighway are in most cases too low. The Hollywood Freeway, built to carry 120,000 cars a day by 1970, was getting twice that much traffic five years earlier. And the New Jersey Turnpike found itself handling on its opening day the load projected for 23 years later.

On the Interstate System itself, even this weight of traffic rarely presents any problems. Quite the opposite; once the car driver fights his way from the infuriating tangle of normal suburban traffic on to the long entrance ramp of an Interstate highway, he can push the speedometer right up to the legal limit and race from the East Coast clear to the Mississippi river without ever hitting a traffic light. For a lorry driver, the highway can provide an even greater blessing: on a test run between Schenectady and Buffalo over the New York State Thruway, a lorry saved 38 miles of travel, 12 gallons of fuel, 298 gear shifts, 142 brake applications, 69 complete stops, and a time total of 4 hours and 29 minutes over the old route. Whether in a lorry or car, the driver is twice as safe on a controlled-access highway, where the fatality rate of 2.7 persons per 100 million vehicle miles is about half the national average of five persons.

Nevertheless, the superhighway, for all its wonders, is neither universally loved nor unreservedly beneficial. No matter how hard the engineers try, a highway is not always a thing of beauty: "In many parts of the country the building of a highway has about the same result upon vegetation and human structures as the passage of a tornado or the blast of an atom bomb", says critic Lewis Mumford. Even a beautiful highway, where it acts as a divider of living zones, can also be a virtually impassable Chinese wall which cuts a town in two, splits a farmer's fields, pollutes the atmosphere, and causes more disruption to some communities that it can soon repay by luring new industry.

Far more crucial to the future mobility of the nation, however, is a peculiar phenomenon which has grown up with the superhighway—traffic breeding. The more traffic a highway can handle, the more traffic it creates. By promoting economic growth along its flanks, the superhighway actually attracts more vehicles. Once these vehicles turn off the highway, they come to a screeching, honking halt in the narrow, grid-pattern streets of the average town. Looking for a quick way out, most towns have hurried to build bigger, wider streets and more car parks.

Too many roads

But in a city like Detroit, 33 per cent of the city is already surfaced. "We're *drowning* out here in superhighways", says one firmly anonymous auto executive. So are a lot of other cities where the demands of a single form of transportation, the motor-car, have taken precedence over the long-range needs of the community as a whole. The answer, for sheer lack of space, cannot be found in building more roadways. The answer, if there is one, lies in a fresh look at the over-all needs of the community both in transportation and in the social purposes which that transportation is designed to serve.

A Nation
on Wheels

More than any other people in history, Americans live on wheels. They travel an average of about 6,000 miles per person per year, almost all of it in that fast, comfortable, convenient instrument, the family car. In fact, it sometimes seems that everything America does is in some way connected with the motor-car. Virtually every baby born in the U.S. makes his triumphant return from the maternity ward in a car. Growing up, he rides to school in a car or bus. His food, his clothes, even the materials to build the house he lives in, roll into his life in a car or on a lorry. As a teenager he pesters his parents to lend him the family's proudest possession for Saturday night dates. When he starts a regular job, there is an 82 per cent chance that he will ride to and from work in a car. His recreation, whether it be a drive to town, like the suburban-ites heading into New York via the Lincoln Tunnel on a winter evening, on the right, a holiday in the Rockies, or just a drive to the nearest beach, will almost certainly involve a motor vehicle. As his life progresses, he will allot 12 per cent of his expenditures and 13 per cent of the space in his house to his car. And finally, there is the grim but inescapable fact that his last ride will be in the back of a rubber-tyred hearse.

SHOPPING IN CARS, Americans pack the parking spaces of huge retailing complexes such as the 500-acre Southdale centre outside Minneapolis, on the left, where department stores, a drive-in bank, supermarkets and an adjacent cinema attract 30,000 customers a day. One of the country's largest, most appealing shopping centres, Southdale has drawn as many as 75,000 window-shoppers on a Sunday when all its stores were closed. Across the U.S., in Southdale and the nation's other 16,000 shopping centres, Americans spend £27,000 million a year.

To reach the stores, housewives, like the young mother below towing her brood behind a shopping basket, drive 49,000 million miles each year—and make 10 million telephone calls to garages to rescue their ailing cars. At night the cash registers ring at thousands of roadside bowling centres, driving ranges, and the nation's 4,500 drive-in theatres. On the next page, a caravan of motor homes clusters in a glow of headlights in Great Falls, Montana. Owners drove to the rendezvous from all parts of the country.

EATING AND SLEEPING along the highway,
American motorists support a nation-wide network of
motels and roadside cafés whose garish signs
call the traveller to rest. Some 42,000 motor courts
have sprouted along U.S. highways, ranging from
60-bed beach courts like those advertised in Lake
George, New York (*right*), to 1,000-bed luxury motels
—complete with heated swimming pools, dog kennels
and miniature golf courses. Even more relentless has
been the spread of eating places, from car-hop
hamburger parlours (*below*) to gourmet roadside inns.
With 100 million cars, lorries and buses now in
operation in the U.S., a total of about £2,500 million is
spent annually on roadside food and overnight
accommodation. So important to the American
economy has the motor-car become that its
manufacture, purchase and upkeep account for one
dollar of every six in the country's cash registers.

WORKING WHEELS, like these long-distance vans lined up
outside an all-night diner at New Haven, Connecticut, provide
jobs for one million Americans. Many van drivers log as much as
100,000 miles a year. For long hauls, like a transcontinental
run which normally takes five or six days, they are often
double-teamed, one driver taking a four-hour turn at the wheel,
while the other grabs catnaps on a mattress in the back of the cab.
Van-driving is hard, demanding work, but the pay is good: a
skilled hand at the wheel can make more than £9,000 a year.

CAR WORSHIP achieves a peak of intensity with the 40,000 stock-car races (*top, right*) around the country, and with such events as the Grand Prix of Endurance at Sebring, Florida (*below, right*), a 12-hour grind over an abandoned airfield. Every year 39 million people flock to car races, more than to all the baseball or football games in the U.S. A whole new language and literature, expressed in a gaudy array of magazines with four million circulation, have developed around the motor-car. Among enthusiasts the veneration of the car is so intense that some cars, like the £9,500 "show car" (seen below, on the far right), an 800-horsepower oddity that can hit 150 m.p.h., are designed mainly to be gazed at rather than to be raced.

America's motor mania engulfs the cities, bringing 340,000 cars into the centre of Los Angeles and 230,000 cars into Chicago every day—

many that all storage space on the ground is used up and the cars must be stacked on top of one another, as in this 14-storey garage in Chicago.

6
Hurdling
Nature's Obstacles

High above the Straits of Mackinac construction workers check a suspension cable on the 1.63-mile Mackinac Bridge, which, by eliminating the wait for a ferry, cuts as much as 20 hours off a trip from Lower to Upper Michigan.

ON THE NIGHT of the 29th December 1876, the wind blew stinging clouds of snow through the gorge of Ashtabula Creek, Ohio, as the westbound *Pacific Express* rumbled on to the span across the deep ravine. Half way over, engineer Dan McGuire had the sudden, terrifying impression that his train was "running uphill". Sensing the awful truth, McGuire threw the throttle wide open. The locomotive surged ahead, snapping the drawbar which coupled it to a second engine and 11 carriages full of people. McGuire's engine, free of its load, scooted safely across. But the rest of the train plunged with the collapsing bridge 69 feet down into the creek-bed. Stoves in the shattered carriages burst open, and by the time the horrified engineer could stop his locomotive and run back to the edge of the gorge, 80 people were dead or dying in the flames, which cast an eerie light through the swirling snow.

Not long after, near Hartford, Connecticut, two locomotives and four carriages went through a rickety bridge over the river Farmington, drowning 17 people beneath the river ice. Though the public was appalled at these tragedies, nobody was really surprised. In the 1870's and '80's, an average of 25 spans per year had let go beneath the weight of freight and passenger trains. Part of the fault lay with the penny-pinching profiteers who built some of the railways: "Our practice", admitted one bridge contractor, "is to put in temporary trestle work . . . which trestle work is renewed . . . and built after the railroad is running". But the basic problem was neither corner-cutting contractors nor their employers. Rather, it was a disastrous lag in the science of bridge building. The power of steam had propelled the wheels of land transportation into a whole new dimension of speed and power. However, there had been no matching progress in supplying long-span bridges which could safely carry a thundering 30-ton locomotive over deep ravines and broad rivers. And until there was, neither these locomotives nor the immense flood of cars and trucks which were to follow could provide the safe, fast transportation, the degree of over-all mobility which society would demand. For bridges are the vital links which bind together a nation's system of land transportation. Lacking bridges, railways and highways are no more than a clutter of almost useless rights-of-way, broken every few miles by deep rivers, and long, slow ferry rides, or shallow streams to ford.

Up to the 19th century, bridge designers still followed ancient patterns. They built most bridges along Roman or Renaissance lines. The former type supported the roadways with semicircular arches which rested on ponderous piers of masonry. This design was adequate for road traffic over a narrow stream where a single arch could easily span the distance between both banks, or for a shallow river where it was easy to make foundations for midstream piers. But on a river with any commercial shipping, midstream piers on a Roman arch are so thick (about one-third the length of the arch) that they may constrict the river channel into a boiling sluiceway through which no boat can safely navigate. Furthermore, while the arches are being built, they must be supported by lattices of timber falsework, which block the river altogether.

And, of course, on a broad, deep river where piers cannot be sunk, the Roman design is worthless: a semicircular arch is half as high from the water line as it is wide, so that a 500-foot span would have to rise 250 feet above the water. Even if it were possible to put up such an immense arch, the approach ramps from a low embankment would be so steep that no horse—and later no locomotive—could make the gradient.

The wider arches of the Renaissance—each a segment of a semicircle— interfered less with the waterway, and permitted lower approach ramps. But the slender stone spans, and the cast-iron arches which followed, were adequate for no more than horse-drawn vehicles. Nor were the early trusses—straight spans made up of interlocking triangular braces— much better. For when these flimsy bridges tried to carry the rumbling traffic of the Industrial Revolution, the results were frequently tragic. Only three years after the Ashtabula wreck, another railway-bridge catastrophe sent 75 travellers to their death when a string of iron spans let go on a stormy December night, dumping the entire train into the black waters of the Firth of Tay in Scotland.

Whiskey-barrel navy

One of the first men to work effectively to end this slaughter was James Buchanan Eads, an energetic, supremely confident American with the most bizarre background for bridge building of anyone who ever put up a span. Eads began his career in St. Louis at the age of 18, when he started out as a clerk on a series of Mississippi side-wheelers. These river packets were frail vessels, and when one of them hit a snag the boat often sank. Smelling a potential profit in salvage, Eads converted a whiskey barrel into a crude diving bell and went down into the river to pick over the bones of a sunken vessel. As the American Civil War approached, he had transformed his whiskey barrel into a fleet of 10 primitive iron submarines, and had become known as the man to call if your boat went down.

When the War began, he did a little calling of his own, to the federal government, and offered to design a fleet of ironclad surface vessels to break Confederate blockades on the Southern rivers. Eads built the ironclads, which blasted Fort Henry into submission, then joined Admiral Farragut at Vicksburg to cut the Confederacy in two.

When the War ended, Eads jumped at a contract to build a railway bridge across the river at St. Louis. He had never before built as much as a foot-bridge, but he knew the water and the bottom of that stretch of Mississippi better than any other man. Furthermore, he had a working knowledge of the structural properties of iron; and this knowledge convinced him that iron should not be used for the major supporting members of a long-span railway bridge. Cast iron was too brittle; wrought iron—more flexible, and far stronger—was better. But at St. Louis, Eads gambled his future, and the lives of many, many people, on a metal for which mass-production methods had just been developed. That metal was called steel; its strength was even greater than wrought iron, and so elastic that a 20-foot girder 8 inches deep could bend 12 inches and

AN ANCIENT ARCH BRIDGE, erected by the Romans in 62 B.C., was one of the seven that carried pedestrians and chariots across the river Tiber. Called the Fabricius Bridge after the Roman commissioner of roads, it was built of huge stones held together by their own weight, without mortar. The two main arches, each spanning about 80 feet, were supported by a central pier 33 feet thick. The strong, graceful structure, shown above as it appeared in the mid-18th century, still stands today.

spring back with no permanent distortion.

Eads confidently planned a bridge of three steel arches, the centre span 520 feet long. Since he knew that he would not be allowed to block the river with complicated falsework, he proposed to put up his arches by the bold method known as cantilevering. In this construction technique, each arm of an arch is built outwards from its pier, with the weight of the arms held up by steel cables anchored on the piers, until the tips of the arms touch to form the finished arch. The experts were aghast. Steel had never before been used for any major structure, let alone a bridge. And if that were not enough, no one had ever tried to cantilever a 520-foot span. "I cannot consent to imperil my reputation by appearing to encourage or approve [the design's] adoption", huffed one engineer who had been invited to join the enterprise. "I deem it entirely unsafe and impractical."

Eads went ahead anyway. But he went ahead slowly, since not even he was sure how he was going to plant his piers on bed-rock which lay as much as 130 feet beneath the muck, the wreckage and the five-to-nine-m.p.h. current of the Mississippi. He found his method during a visit to Europe, where he discovered that a French engineer had excavated for bridge piers 75 feet below the surface of the river at Piacenza, Italy, protected by a bottomless iron box called a caisson, filled with compressed air. The air pressure, delivered by hoses and pipes from above, kept out the river water while the men dug at the mud underfoot.

Horror of the bends

For the St. Louis project, Eads built three caissons, one of which had seven air locks. Inside each caisson was an ingenious system of pumps which sucked up the river-bottom ooze and carried it to a dumping platform on the surface. The caissons seemed a perfect inspiration—until one man who had been digging at a depth of 100 feet dropped dead 15 minutes after leaving the air lock. As the work progressed, 13 more men died and 2 were permanently crippled. Neither Eads nor the doctors he engaged were able to pin-point the cause of the affliction, which came to be called the bends, or find a cure. As is known today, the cause was a sudden release of nitrogen bubbles in the bloodstream and fatty tissues when the men came directly from the 25-to-50-pounds-per-square-inch pressure of the working chamber into the normal 14.7 pounds of sea-level atmosphere. The solution was slow decompression requiring up to an hour. But this solution was many years and many lives away.

Nevertheless, the work went forward. The piers were finished and the cantilevered sections of the great arches began to reach out across the river. When at last the halves of one arch met in September of 1873, they turned out to be three and a half inches too long for a proper fit. A daring young supervisor named Theodore Cooper tried to carry out the notion of packing the rib ends in ice to shrink the metal. In 30 hours, 60 tons of ice was packed in troughs around the metal in a huge, sodden poultice. "We were so sleepy," said Cooper later, "that it was impossible

AN ANCIENT SUSPENSION BRIDGE, developed by the Inca of Peru in the 15th century, was a practical solution to the enormous problem of crossing the deep gorges of the Andes Mountains. The Inca pulled thick cables of braided twigs across the gorges, anchored the cables to stone piers and fastened small sticks crosswise over the cables to serve as a walkway. Although they seemed insubstantial, these swaying bridges carried a heavy traffic of men and animals.

to keep our eyes open, and I was afraid some of us would go into the river." (Cooper himself later did, and survived the 90-foot plunge.) But this immense repacking still left the arch an agonizing three-quarters of an inch too long, and Cooper's crew had to instal a whole new segment.

The bridge which Cooper helped to finish was the largest in the world up to that time—1,524 feet from bank to bank. It was at once the first steel bridge as well as the first major steel structure of any kind in the world. For the first public test, on the 2nd July 1874, Eads sent a procession of 14 locomotives on to the 520-foot-long centre span, which stood up handsomely beneath the load. At the formal opening on the Fourth of July, cannon boomed in salute 100 times and 300,000 spectators shouted their tribute. The *Scientific American* nominated Eads as its President. And the St. Louis bridge, with its cantilevered arches stiffened by a webbing of steel trusses, became the model for a whole series of long spans around the world.

High wire to Brooklyn

Meanwhile another bridge-building drama of a different kind, but of an equally far-reaching nature, was in the making in New York, where the East River separated the business districts of Manhattan from the residences of Brooklyn. Ferry travel had become impossibly slow for the thousands who commuted across the river each day. And when ice clogged the channel in the bitter winter of 1866-1867, a traveller could move by rail from Manhattan to Albany, over 150 miles away, faster than he could get to Brooklyn on the ferry. For decades there had been talk about an East River bridge, but no one had produced a design that properly solved the river's monumental problems: a 1,600-foot-wide channel of surging tide-water traversed each day by a dense stream of ocean shipping. Then, in the same year that Eads proposed his steel arches for the Mississippi, a brilliant German immigrant named John Augustus Roebling was appointed to carry out an even more radical concept for the East River: a suspension bridge which would be supported by four steel cables, each 16 inches in diameter. This bridge would carry two lanes of horse carriages, two cable-car lines and a pedestrian walking way so high above the river that the tallest mast would never touch the roadway.

"Wire cable bridges", Roebling wrote, "properly constructed will be found hereafter the most durable and cheapest . . . bridges for spans over one hundred feet." The reason for their low price—and in fact for their basic advantage as an engineering design—can be seen from a simple comparison: 13 pounds of wire will carry a man's weight over a 100-foot-wide gorge, while a wrought-iron beam would have to weigh 88,000 pounds to carry its own bulk and that of the passenger.

"Any span inside of 3,000 feet is practicable", said Roebling, grandly.

"[And] if the proposed bridge shall possess capacity of 40,000,000 [people] annually, these 40,000,000 will be there as sure as the bridge is built. . . . The contemplated work when constructed in accordance with my designs, will not only be the greatest bridge in existence, but it will be the great engineering work of this Continent and of the age."

Bold words. Not only was Roebling prophesying traffic heavier than the world had yet seen on a span even half that long, he was also proposing to employ a bridge design having an ancient and dishonourable history of failure. The earliest suspension bridges were nothing but pairs of ropes overlaid with planking and slung across the gorges of Peru, China and India. They had a sickening sway and wobble, and frequently they gave way altogether. One in China undulated so terrifyingly that nervous travellers had to be blindfolded, bound to litters and carried over. Of another, put up by the Incas in Peru, a traveller wrote: "This aerial bridge dipped with an alarming inclination towards the centre, while the motion given to it by the passenger occasioned an oscillation even more frightful, as his eye wandered over the dark abyss of waters that foamed and tumbled many a fathom beneath."

Death on the river

Later experiments with heavy-traffic suspension bridges were hardly reassuring. In 1850, 200 French infantrymen, marching in cadence over a suspension span at Angers, crashed through to their death. Four years later, a new suspension bridge at Wheeling, West Virginia, began swaying in a gale of wind, and its oscillations multiplied until the entire span tumbled into the river Ohio. Against this background, Roebling's pronouncements had an alarming—if not lunatic—ring. However, the shaggy-browed, strong-minded engineer had a formidable record of success in everything he undertook and a way of persuading even his most caustic critics.

Born and educated in Germany, John Roebling began his career in America in 1837 as an assistant engineer and surveyor for a series of Pennsylvania canal and railway builders. During the course of his work he developed America's first wire rope, which he sold to the canal companies for hauling heavy barges over mountain portages. By 1844 he was head of a thriving wire-rope factory and he used his own wire-rope cables to put up his first suspension bridge, an aqueduct carrying an entire section of a barge canal with its 1,900 tons of water over the river Allegheny at Pittsburgh. For this job Roebling borrowed a new technique from the French engineer Louis Vicat and assembled thousands of wires into two seven-inch cables of parallel strands right on the site itself, stringing the 1,900 wires for each cable one by one over the bridge towers. Roebling immediately followed the Pittsburgh project with

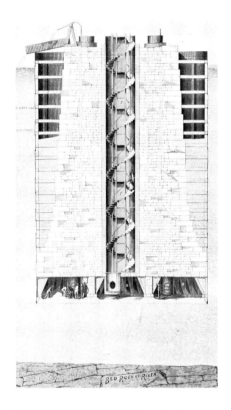

BUILDING A BRIDGE PIER under deep water was made possible by the pneumatic caisson, shown here in a drawing of work on James Eads's St. Louis span. The masonry pier was erected inside the rectangular caisson (*above*), directly on top of its excavation chamber (*enlarged below*). This chamber, a bottomless box resting on the river floor, was filled with compressed air to keep water out while workers dug away the river-bed. As the foundation hole deepened, the caisson moved down until it and the pier rested on bed-rock, forming a sturdy support for the bridge.

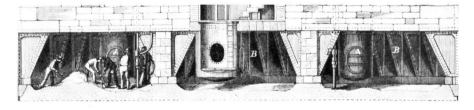

a highway suspension bridge, its roadway stiffened against wind and traffic vibrations by timber trusses and wire-rope stays. Then, in 1851, he moved in on the world's boldest bridge project up to that time: a railway bridge soaring 821 feet in one single span over the 245-foot-deep chasm below Niagara Falls.

On either side of the gorge he put up a masonry tower, and between them he spun four wrought-iron cables, each with 3,640 wires. From the cables he suspended a double-decked roadway, the upper deck for railway trains, the lower for carriages and pedestrians. Between the two decks, which were 18 feet apart, Roebling put in a latticework of iron trusses. And finally, he stabilized the span even more with a webbing of 64 stays from the tower tops to the lower roadway. In its first test, on the 6th March 1855, the bridge safely carried a test train of double-loaded freight cars weighing 327 tons. And because of the efficiency of the suspension principle, the price tag for the Niagara project was a very modest £175,000 (compared to the £3,000,000 which Eads would eat up erecting his massive steel arches at St. Louis). Quickly, lest the other lessons of Niagara be lost, Roebling wrote them down:

A careful warning

". . . weight, Girders, Trusses and Stays. With these any degree of stiffness can be insured, to resist either the action of trains, or the violence of storms, or even hurricanes. . . . And I will here observe that no Suspension Bridge is safe without some of these appliances. The catalogue of disastrous failures is now large enough to warn against light fabrics, suspended to be blown down. . . . A number of such fairy creations are still hovering about the country, only waiting for a rough blow to be demolished."

Then, looking ahead to his plan for the proposed Brooklyn project, he wrote, "A span of 1,600 feet or more can be made just as safe, and as strong in proportion as a span of 100 feet. . . . To guard against vertical and horizontal oscillations, and to insure that degree of stiffness essential to meet the violent gales in such exposed conditions, I have provided six lines of iron trusses, which run the whole length of the suspended floor from anchor wall to anchor wall".

The Brooklyn Bridge authorities were convinced, and John Roebling began making his pier surveys. He never finished. On the 28th June 1869, he was standing on a Brooklyn wharf taking a sighting when a ferryboat rammed into the dock, crushing Roebling's foot between the timbers. The fractures became infected, and in three weeks John Roebling, the most imaginative bridge builder of his day and, to many minds, the greatest civil engineer of the entire 19th century, was dead. However, the Roebling name and the Brooklyn project continued to grow—together. In a poignant deathbed scene, John Roebling handed over the supervision of the Brooklyn Bridge to the one man who would be certain to carry it through: 32-year-old Colonel Washington Roebling, a cool-headed combat officer in the Civil War, co-builder with his father of a spectacular

RIVER-BED WORKERS who excavated the eastern pier of the Brooklyn Bridge approached their jobs through an airlock (*above*), designed to prevent loss of air pressure. When the workers had entered the lock, they sealed it by closing the hatch above their heads. Then they opened the bottom hatch and descended into the pressurized chamber (*below*). This room was so large that 100 men worked at a time, digging up boulders and clay and carting the rubble to a removal shaft.

suspension span at Cincinnati, and the eldest son of the dying genius.

Pulling together all the lessons his father had learned at Niagara and Allegheny, and adding a few forward-looking notions of his own, Washington Roebling hurled himself into the Brooklyn project with the immense energy characteristic of his clan. To get his piers down to bed-rock, the son built two massive caissons, drawing on the careful observations he had made on a recent visit to Eads's St. Louis construction. The Brooklyn caissons were made of 12-by-12-inch pine beams, caulked with oakum and coated with pitch, and roofed over with 15 to 22 feet of timber. As places to work, they were even more hellish than the ones at St. Louis. A master carpenter described his impressions of work in one of the caissons: "Inside . . . everything wore an unreal, weird appearance. What with the flaming lights, the deep shadows, the confusing noise of hammers, drills and chains, the half-naked forms flitting about, with here and there a Sisyphus rolling his stone, one might, if of a poetic temperament, get a realizing sense of Dante's inferno".

The infernal atmosphere was intensified in December 1870, when a candle set too close to an oakum seam started a smouldering fire that ate four feet into the roof. Roebling came down into the caisson himself to fight the fire. He stayed seven hours, then he was carried out unconscious. He recovered, but in the spring of 1872 he went down once too often, and by winter the bends had rendered him a lifetime cripple, in constant pain and with only the barest whisper of a voice.

Proxy command

However, nothing was going to stop Washington Roebling from finishing the project his father had started. From a balcony of his house overlooking the river, he watched the work through field glasses and dictated instructions to his wife, Emily, who relayed them to the men. Under this proxy command, five years were needed to finish the towers, and another year to spin the 21,736 oil-coated, galvanized steel wires for the main cables. When the last strands were in place, the cables were compacted by powerful clamps and wrapped with a softer wire. The roadway was then laid down, strengthened by iron and steel stays which alone would have supported the deck if the cable parted. On the 24th May 1883, 14 years after the fateful ferry-boat accident, the Brooklyn Bridge was completed.

At the opening ceremonies, keynote speaker Abram S. Hewitt, Congressman from New York, moistened many an eye with his throbbing eulogy of the builders: "Death, indeed, was the fate of its great projector, and dread disease the heritage of the great engineer who had brought it to completion". Editor Alfred Ely Beach of *Scientific American*, turning his fickle back on Eads's St. Louis structure, pronounced the Brooklyn Bridge "the grandest piece of engineering the world has yet seen". President Chester A. Arthur confidently walked across the record-breaking 1,595-foot span. As the ceremony rambled on, Colonel Washington Roebling watched through his field glasses on Columbia Heights. Later that afternoon, a part of the crowd, led by the politicians, marched to Co-

BACK-BREAKING LABOUR, the difficult task of digging out rock-filled clay for the foundation at the Brooklyn end of the Brooklyn Bridge is shown in these drawings from *Scientific American*. Boulders had to be drilled for blasting (*above*), and hard-packed clay had to be broken up. The rubble was pushed under the foot of a shaft (*below*), its opening kept under water so that compressed air could not escape from the chamber. Inside the shaft a train of buckets scooped the material up to the surface.

lumbia Heights to pay personal homage to the courageous man who had brought his father's plan to fruition.

The homage was deserved. For in the developing science of long-span bridge building, the Roeblings' great achievement was the giant step that enabled the world's wheels to leave behind the slow ways of the horse-drawn era for the surging traffic of the 20th century, when each day millions of vehicles would demand swift passage over the broadest rivers. While economics and the sheer weight of steel put a practical limit of 1,500 to 1,800 feet on spans of cantilevers and trussed arches, the principles of suspension established at Brooklyn cleared the way for the far longer structures John Roebling had prophesied. In 1931 engineer Othmar H. Ammann hung the 50,000-ton deck of the George Washington Bridge over the river Hudson in a single span of 3,500 feet. Six years later the Golden Gate Bridge leaped 4,200 feet from pier to pier across the entrance to San Francisco Bay. Finally, in 1965, using no more than refinements on the techniques of the Roeblings (but with steel one-third to one-half stronger), Ammann completed the longest one of all, the 4,260-foot centre span of the Verrazano-Narrows Bridge over the mouth of New York Harbor.

Galloping Gertie

As engineers reached out to create these slim, elegant structures, their vision at one point became so dazzled by the artistry of bridge building that they lost sight of a crucial bit of its science. In 1940 the Tacoma Narrows Bridge was flung across the wind-swept waters of Puget Sound with nothing more than an eight-foot deck girder to stiffen the 2,800-foot main span. Some critics called it the most beautiful bridge in the world. Motorists called it Galloping Gertie, because of the rolling, twisting motion it took on in moderate breezes. Gertie was so flexible, in fact, that even on a relatively still day a motorist crossing the bridge sometimes noticed the car in front apparently sinking into the deck and even disappearing momentarily from view. Some engineers solemnly explained the advantages of a flexible roadway, and laymen thought Gertie's antics were all quite amusing until the day, only four months after she was opened that Gertie galloped herself to smithereens in a 40-m.p.h. wind.

Three distinguished engineers, including Othmar H. Ammann, spent four and a half months investigating the cause of Gertie's demise. Their voluminous report declared, in essence, that Gertie was aerodynamically unstable. And their analysis of that instability was an elaborate, 20th-century version of John Roebling's reaction to the Wheeling Bridge disaster 86 years earlier: "That bridge was destroyed by the momentum acquired by its own dead weight, when swayed up and down by the force of the wind. . . . A high wind, acting upon a suspended floor, devoid of inherent stiffness, will produce a series of undulations . . . [and these] undulations . . . will increase to a certain extent by their own effort, until by a steady blow a momentum of force may be produced that may prove stronger than the cable. And [the bridge will] work its own destruction".

Today, long before the excavations for the piers of a major suspension span begin, a model of the bridge is tested in a wind tunnel, and the results of the test, together with reams of information on anticipated traffic loadings, high and low temperatures for the region, etc., are fed into a computer for analysis. At the Massachusetts Institute of Technology in the U.S., in fact, an engineer planning a bridge can make a sketch with a light-projecting pen on the screen of a television-like tube which is linked to a computer. The computer then whips the sketch into a geometrically correct drawing, and a high-speed printing device gives out the figures on stresses in that bridge.

With such exotic new techniques at their disposal, engineers around the world have launched the greatest bridge-building binge in history. In the U.S. alone, some 3,000 spans go up across the country each year at a cost of £630 million. There are 729 bridges on the 559 miles of the New York Thruway, and one dollar of every three spent on the new Interstate Highway System goes into a bridge.

Longer and stronger

As they put up these thousands upon thousands of new bridges, designers are continually searching for stronger, lighter, more economical kinds of spans. One new design, recently borrowed from Germany, has been applied at St. Louis to the Poplar Street Bridge, and to San Francisco's newest Bay Bridge, whose so-called orthotropic structure makes the steel deck plate serve as both the bridge floor and the upper flange of the supporting girders. The slender structure of orthotropic bridges is inherently so strong that the decking supports itself for distances of more than 800 feet, thus saving as much as half the steel used to hold up the running surface. By eliminating deep trusses, an orthotropic bridge also permits flatter approach ramps and greater clearances for shipping.

Another ingenious, relatively new technique involves the use of pre-stressed concrete. By embedding finger-thick steel wires under tension into a slim concrete beam, a bridge builder can create a supporting member which is as strong as any all-steel beam. The first major pre-stressed concrete bridge in the world crossed the river Mulde in Zwickau, Germany in 1936. One of the longest is Venezuela's magnificent, five-and-a-half-mile General Rafael Urdaneta Bridge, its five main spans of pre-stressed concrete, each 771 feet long, tying the oil city of Maracaibo to the eastern coastal belt and the mineral-rich mountains of the interior.

Even the suspension bridge may be ready to make another jump in length. With the refined techniques now at his command, a designer can put up a bridge with the same load-carrying capacity per traffic lane as, for example, the 3,800-foot Straits of Mackinac span, but using only 60 per cent of the weight of the steel. There is talk of joining Italy with Sicily across the Strait of Messina, perhaps with a record-breaking 4,900-foot span. "I don't think a bridge of 10,000 feet is impossible", says one New York engineer. "I tell people we put up bridges that will last 1,000 years", says another. "But I'm not sure they couldn't last for ever."

John Roebling would have approved.

The Art
of Bridge Building

Without bridges the wheels of the world could scarcely roll at all. Sooner or later every roadway encounters a river, a valley or some other natural impasse; unless ways were found to cross these barriers, whole regions might be virtually isolated—while vast traffic jams of cars and trains piled up at the land's end. To keep the wheels rolling, the U.S. alone has built some 500,000 bridges, ranging in length from the spectacular 4,260-foot centre span of New York's great Verrazano down to humble 20-foot highway bridges (anything shorter is considered not a bridge but a culvert).

Whatever their lengths, each of these spans is individually built to solve the special problems posed by a particular kind of obstacle. Thus, if the roadway must reach over a long open space with no intervening supports, the most practical form may be the suspension design, in which the travelling surface hangs from steel cables held by massive towers; if the span is relatively short, a simple beam of reinforced concrete will do. Between these two extremes there is a dramatic gallery of other bridge forms, each made of materials that are carefully matched to its special shape and construction problems—and each carrying a vital burden of wheeled vehicles.

THE POWER OF SUSPENSION
Cables dipping down from a pair of steel towers carried a record 57 million vehicles in 1965 across the 3,500-foot main span of the George Washington Bridge between New York City and New Jersey. Because of the high cost of building the supporting towers, a suspension bridge is usually uneconomical unless the main span is at least 1,500 feet long.

New Dimensions for an Old Form

For generations, Staten Island, New York, lying only a few hundred feet from the New Jersey mainland on one side, and a few thousand from the rest of New York on the other, remained a drowsy exurb, cut off by a barrier of salt water. Then between 1928 and 1931 three bridges were put in, the most spectacular a 1,652-foot steel arch (*left*) connecting the island to Bayonne, New Jersey. Like any arch, the Bayonne structure gets its strength from its carefully planned curve, which redirects the downward load on the span outwards to supporting abutments at either end.

This world-record arch, together with its sister bridges, tied Staten Island to the industry of North Jersey, and, with the addition of the Verrazano-Narrows Bridge in 1964 providing an eastward link to Brooklyn, the sleepy island has been changed into a bustling urban community.

VARIATIONS ON A THEME

The roadway of the Bayonne Bridge (*left*) hangs by cables from the supporting arch, whose steel ribs are further strengthened by triangular braces called trusses. By contrast, Germany's Fehmarnsund Bridge (*above*), completed in 1963 to shorten travelling time to Denmark, uses structural steel in the roadway to tie together the ends of each arch. This helps to keep the structure from sagging under its load. The cross-hatched cables simultaneously support the deck and act as a light-weight truss; inward tipping of the arches cuts the cost of transverse bracing.

Italian designers faced a difficult problem running a highway over wildly uneven ground between Florence and Bologna. They solved

THREE IN ONE

The utility of reinforced concrete for short and medium spans is demonstrated in Italy's San Giuliano Bridge. The arch, girders and centre span of the deck were poured in a single mould, producing a strong, handsome bridge. Before the use of reinforced concrete, the major parts had to be made separately, then laboriously joined together at the building site.

TWO IN ONE

The deck and girders of Switzerland's curving Schwandbach Bridge, built in 1933, were designed as a unit. This section was then laid on top of a slim but immensely strong concrete arch.

it by building a series of viaducts. This one has eight concrete arches, each moulded into six piers and stiffened by a system of struts.

Moulded Bridges
for Motor-Cars

With 230 million cars, lorries and buses now rolling around the world, engineers are pressed to develop quicker, cheaper ways of building bridges. The heavier demand has been for the shorter spans which abound on modern highways (the U.S. Interstate Highway System will have some 60,000 such bridges).

An outstanding response to this need has come from reinforced concrete. Though concrete is easy to mould into any structural shape, it needs reinforcement because of its vulnerability to tension. Tension is generated by the loads on a straight, simple span, for the weight tends to bend the deck so that the bottom sections are stretched. To add tensile strength, the concrete is reinforced by a network of steel rods and wire mesh. This steel is placed in a mould whose shape is calculated to help to absorb the various stresses. This shape may be an arch to assist in supporting the deck beams. When everything is ready, the engineer simply pours his concrete into the form; when it is dry, his bridge is built.

Leaping
Lakes and Oceans

To span really great distances with concrete, bridge engineers had to wait until relatively recent times for a technique that was neither too ponderous nor too expensive. Meanwhile, vehicles had to follow circuitous routes. Travellers approaching New Orleans from the north often had to travel more than 60 miles around Lake Pontchartrain to reach the heart of the city, although the actual direct-line distance was only about 30 miles.

Then bridge builders began using an ingenious method of strengthening concrete called pre-stressing, which permits the casting of concrete beams as long and slender as beams of steel. Instead of filling most of the concrete mould with a complex network of bars and mesh, as with reinforced concrete, the designer casts his beams with a series of lengthwise strands of steel wire clamping the beam, end to end. These wires hold together the particles of concrete so that the forces of tension cannot pull the beam apart. The result is a very strong, stable structure capable of spanning chasms of more than 700 feet with no intervening support. Better still, this strength is produced with less than half the steel and perhaps 80 per cent as much concrete as is needed for conventional reinforced construction.

In 1956 builders completed the first of two concrete bridges that stretch 24 miles across Lake Pontchartrain to link downtown New Orleans directly with the north shore.

OVER AN INLAND SEA
One of the two pre-stressed Lake Pontchartrain causeways (*left*), the world's longest highway bridges, stretches to the horizon of the shallow lake near New Orleans. For eight miles of the 24-mile crossing, travellers between the city and the lake's north shore do not see land.

OVER THE OYSTER BEDS
In the bridge on the right, thin beams of pre-stressed concrete, measuring up to 250 feet between piers, reach out a mile from the French coast to the island of Oléron. A favourite of tourists, Oléron is also an oyster centre and the bridge speeds the oysters to the mainland.

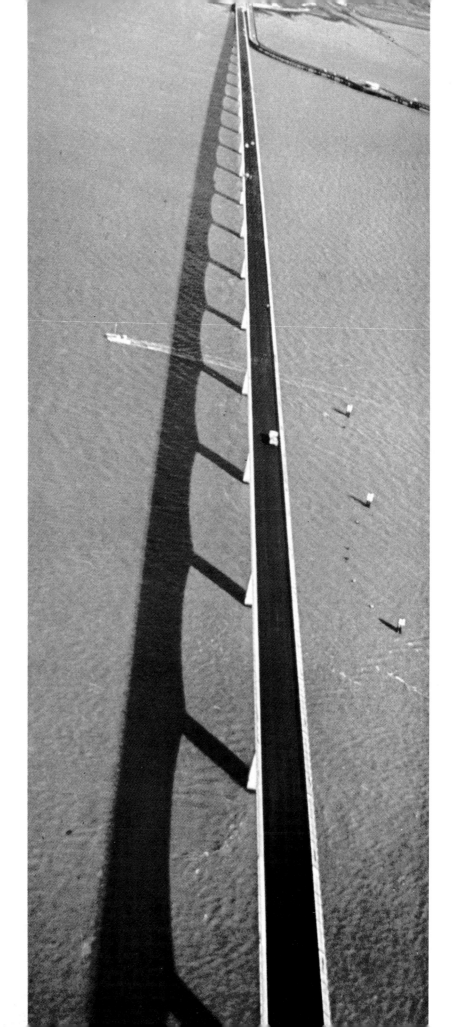

Floating on a Floor of Concrete

The land around Seattle, Washington, is cleft into quarters by three bodies of water: the 200-foot-deep Lake Washington, an estuary called the Hood Canal, and the tide-swept waters of Puget Sound. Without an ingenious system of bridges, traffic could not flow among the different sections of the city, and great portions of the urban complex would be cut off from the farms and woodlands in the north and from the industrial region to the south. But when the bridges shown on these pages were first projected, both the lake and the canal were found to be too deep to take the supporting piers of a suspension bridge and too wide for any kind of arch.

Faced with this impasse, Seattle decided to float its bridges on pontoons, so that the whole of every span could be supported by the water it was crossing. One of them, over the Hood Canal, goes over more than a mile of open water, its roadway resting on 23 huge hollow-chambered pontoons made of pre-stressed concrete. To keep the roadway from floating away altogether, the bridge is tethered by some 16 miles of cable hooked into the 800-ton concrete anchors.

A SLIDING SANDWICH OF CONCRETE
The newest of Seattle's floating bridges, the 7,578-foot Evergreen Point Bridge, has a unique 200-foot drawbridge section for deep-sea vessels. When a ship approaches, a portion at either end of the drawbridge section is lifted seven feet. Then the adjacent pontoons slide neatly back beneath the elevated sections in order to open the waterway to the vessel. The whole operation can be done in six to eight minutes, from the time vehicles are first stopped until the two halves are rejoined and the roadway is clear again for cars, lorries and buses.

OPEN FOR SHIPPING

The drawbridge sections of the Hood Canal Bridge were too big to raise up to let shipping pass. So the engineers designed the midsection of the 4-lane road in an hour-glass shape. When a vessel approaches, the waist portions of the hour-glass retract into the bulges at either end.

OPEN FOR CARS

After the ship has passed, the two halves of the Hood's drawbridge section slide back together, clearing the roadway for the 50,000 cars that cross it each day. The floating bridge has withstood gale winds of 80 m.p.h.; and, in fact, bad weather has never disrupted traffic across it.

A New Shape for an Urgent Need

At the end of World War II, West Germany faced the challenge of restoring some 4,800 demolished bridges. And there was very little steel—or money—at hand for the task. Out of sheer necessity, German designers created wholly new bridge forms, economical enough to fit within their budgets, but strong enough to carry the nation's rising tide of traffic.

One of the most striking of these new designs is the bridle-cord bridge shown here, in which a slender roadway of steel or pre-stressed concrete is partially supported by slim steel wires. The remainder of the support comes from the strength of the deck and girders themselves. Bridle-cord construction, which has been adopted in other countries, saves up to 50 per cent of the steel that a conventional suspension bridge requires.

A SOUTH AMERICAN SPAN

Venezuela applied the bridle-cord suspension idea to a 5½-mile bridge over Lake Maracaibo. Five main spans of pre-stressed concrete, each 771 feet, link the city of Maracaibo with the cattle and ore-producing country of the interior.

THE BRIDLE CORD AT HOME

One of the world's longest bridle-cord bridges is the 991-foot main span across the Rhine at Cologne, Germany (*below*). Six wires hung from a single tower (*far left*) help support the steel-girder structure of the bridge's roadway.

The Form of the Future

In the back of every bridge engineer's mind is a slim, strong, utterly beautiful shape which might be called the ultimate bridge. This bridge could carry an avalanche of vehicles over the most awesome natural barrier, and would be easy to erect and inexpensive to complete.

The Europa Bridge on the right, built in the Brenner Pass between Austria and Italy, almost realizes this ideal. It is an example of a post-war design commonly called orthotropic, in which the steel plating of the deck doubles as the upper flange of the supporting girders. This integration of the deck with its supporting members produces a structure so thin yet strong that a 676-foot centre-span bridge in Germany requires a thickness of only 11 feet to carry six lanes of traffic. One bridge in Yugoslavia covers spans of 850 feet without intervening supports.

Within 20 years after the method was first used, there were some 45 long-span orthotropic structures in 15 European nations, a tribute to the appeal of this superb form among engineers seeking the ultimate bridge.

BEAUTY OUT OF STRENGTH
The slender Europa Bridge carries more than 1.5 million cars and lorries per year across the river Sill 600 feet below the roadway. From end to end, the bridge measures 3,700 feet, yet it rests on only six reinforced concrete piers.

144

7

The Dilemmas
of the Business
Centre

An elevated railway with a promenade for strollers was proposed in 1874 as a solution to the congestion that even then clogged Manhattan streets. While this one was not built, others helped (but never cured) New York's traffic ills.

EACH MORNING as the first grey light filters into the eastern sky, the city spreads its arms and beckons to the world. And the world responds. In London the faint growl of the underground rises to a sullen roar as a tidal surge of half a million underground travellers turns towards the heart of the city. In Tokyo and the teeming suburbs around it, four million clerks and shopkeepers climb on to the swift, crowded electric coaches of the Japanese National Railways. At New Delhi, tens of thousands of bicycle riders pour down the broad avenues; in Melbourne, 96,000 move in by trolley. In Los Angeles, epicentre of the American motor-car culture, no less than 1,500,000 drivers start their daily round of over three million motor vehicle trips on freeways in and around the city; while in Manhattan, two million souls scurry towards their urban offices, three-quarters of them by tube, the rest by bus, car, commuter railway and on foot.

"Each great capital", wrote Lewis Mumford in *The Culture of Cities*, "sits like a spider in the midst of its transportation web." Without that web—which not only gets people to and from their work, but also satisfies the enormous appetite of any city for goods and raw materials—the spider-city would very quickly shrivel and die. Just to keep going, these cities demand the transportation of over 3,000 million tons of materials every year—20 tons for every single urban dweller. And every ounce rolls to the consumer on a lorry or a train. Thus the wheel has made the city possible as a place to work and prosper.

But at the same time, by the most unhappy paradox, the wheel has also made the metropolis nearly impossible as a place to live. In the cramped quarters of American cities, each year the appalling total of 73,000 million car trips and 7,000 million transit rides takes place. Only 15 per cent of this car traffic is generated by people moving in or out of the central city; the main weight of the traffic is car and lorry trips made by drivers who already live in town, or who are passing through *en route* to another destination. The crush in the business sections is doubly bad because the basic street patterns for the core of most U.S. cities were laid out 100 or more years ago. The central business district is clustered tightly around the railway terminal; the street pattern of narrow roadways and small blocks was designed for three-m.p.h. horse-drawn wagon traffic. Worse yet, more than half the present-day motor vehicle trips which occur on these narrow thoroughfares are jammed into the four peak travel hours of the morning and evening rush. The result is chaos.

Nor has the U.S. any monopoly on this kind of chaos. In Tokyo the rush-hour crush (which the Japanese call the *rasshu awa*) is so intense that the railway has taken on a regiment of *oshiya-san* (honourable pushers) to shoehorn bodies into the steaming coaches at the end of the day. With typical Oriental courtesy, pushers at some stations give out wooden sandals to commuters whose own footwear has been torn off during the ride. In England, Colin Buchanan, traffic adviser to the British Ministry of Transportation, offered this description of life in London at the rush hour:

"At five o'clock or thereabouts . . . this huge office (and others in the vicinity do likewise) starts to disgorge its occupants. . . . The narrow streets become like rat-runs as hundreds of people scurry along on their homeward journey. . . . At the same time, however, the private cars are unleashed from the office buildings, the factories and warehouses, and from various hidey-holes all over the place, and these start percolating out, eventually to join the stream on some main route. . . . I am one of the rats who make this journey on foot, and I can tell you that I regard the crossing of every street as a potential death trap. . . . The total picture of sordid confusion is quite terrifying."

Blurred picture

The picture has existed almost as long as there have been cities. And for just as long, thoughtful men have been seeking a solution. Some of their most appealing ideas—particularly in urban planning—have a surprisingly modern ring. Julius Caesar tried separating traffic in Rome by time periods: he restricted traffic of wheeled vehicles from the centre during working hours, and permitted the transport of most heavy building materials, rubble and refuse only in the night hours (a very sensible edict which many modern cities are now trying to emulate). In 1483 in Milan, Leonardo da Vinci tried to clear up the vehicular confusion by a physical separation of different kinds of traffic. He proposed a network of double-decked roadways which would completely segregate pedestrians from vehicles. "The high-level roads are not to be used by wagons or like vehicles but are solely for the convenience of the gentlefolk", he wrote. "All carts and loads for the service and convenience of the common people should be confined to the low-level roads." In the mid 17th century Oliver Cromwell attempted to nip London's budding urban tangle by creating a series of so-called "green belts" around the city. Theoretically, these open lands on which building was forbidden would limit the geographic size of the city and thus limit the number of vehicles the city would spawn. But when Cromwell died, so did most of the green belts, joining in limbo Leonardo's separated roadways, Caesar's vehicle-limiting traffic control, and other pieces of planning which, as the urban population exploded, might have prevented the cities' wheels from becoming the cities' frustration. Instead, the emphasis was always on newer, bigger, faster vehicles that were designed to make travel easier but ended simply by making the cities larger and more congested.

That, surely, was the effect of the horse-drawn rail carriages, which appeared in New York in 1832 as an attempted solution to that city's already acute problem of moving people—200,000 of them—in the city area. At the opening of the pioneering Fourth Avenue line, Mayor Walter Bourne predicted, "This event will go down in our history as the greatest achievement of man". Though the horse-trams would hardly do that, they did haul groups of up to 90 people at five m.p.h.—almost twice the speed of regular wagon traffic.

By 1886, 300 U.S. cities had tram lines. Together with the first commuter steam railways, these trams changed the shape of the city. A con-

A STRANGE VEHICLE, powered by horses and holding two layers of passengers, was suggested in 1885 by Frank R. Stockton in a short story called "The Tricycle of the Future". Stockton's imaginary contraption, one of many wild ideas aimed at solving the traffic problems of the 19th century, is shown here as depicted in an illustration for the story. It was driven by a team of horses running on an enormous treadmill; above the horses the passengers sunned themselves on the vehicle's open-air decks.

temporary Bostonian, whose city had previously been limited by slow-moving foot and wagon traffic to 25 densely packed square miles at the edge of the harbour, described the change: "If by horse one can go eight m.p.h.," he wrote of the new rail traffic, "the diameter of the city becomes sixteen miles and the area two hundred and one square miles; and, if by railroad he moves 30 m.p.h., the diameter becomes sixty miles, and the area becomes 2,827. The effect . . . is plainly seen about Boston. . . . People who in 1830 were mostly confined to the city, now live in . . . Cambridge, Charlestown, Somerville . . . and Salem; places distant from two to thirteen miles." This was the beginning of the suburban sprawl, a phenomenon which would keep growing in size and at a speed commensurate with the vehicles that nurtured it.

Though the city was spreading out, the business section, with its tight grid of narrow streets designed not for swift movement of heavy traffic but rather to give horse-wagons easy access to buildings along the roadway, was more congested than ever. Clearly, what was needed was a practical new concept in urban transit, a system which could conveniently move masses of people—but not on the city streets.

Sewer commuters

New York, in an effort to get some of the transit riders off its streets, was putting up a network of elevated railways whose heavy steam-engines shook the frail trestles and showered sparks and soot on both pedestrians and tinder-box tenements. More to the point, they raised some 60 million passengers per year above the crush of city traffic. And in London 10 million people per year had begun riding beneath the streets in a sulphurous, steam-driven shuttle train nicknamed "the sewer". It was a suffocating passage on which decent citizens carried candles to find their way around, indecent ones had a field day picking pockets, and from which one woman passenger emerged still and motionless, pronounced dead of coal-gas asphyxiation.

Despite the hazards and inconveniences, however, both the elevated railway and the sewer railway offered considerable promise as means of mass urban transit. All they required to become both practical and convenient was a clean, powerful engine to pull them. Happily, the form of just such an engine was taking shape in the brains of a handful of brilliant engineers whose passion was electricity. The most effective among them was a cocksure Yankee named Frank J. Sprague.

Sprague took his first important job as an assistant under Thomas Edison at Menlo Park, where he amused himself by careering around on a narrow-gauge railcar rigged up with an old dynamo, rewired to become an electric motor whose current came via the rails from a pair of generators. Like most of the other so-called motors of the day, the converted dynamo was wildly erratic, creeping along with an ominous hum, then suddenly darting off at speeds up to 40 m.p.h. while white-knuckled visitors held on for a ride that was, as one of them recalled 45 years later, "enough to scare the life out of me".

It was also enough to convince Sprague that the real excitement in electricity was in developing motors for traction. He resigned from Menlo Park, set up his own company and built a motor so superior to all its predecessors that Edison, the master, wrote of Sprague's brainchild: "His is the only true motor; the others are but dynamos turned into motors. His machine keeps the same rate of speed all the time, and does not vary with the amount of work done, as the others do."

Now the stage was complete, and ready for Sprague to step on to it. He would have to hurry. East Cleveland had a two-mile experimental electric tram. A brilliant Belgian immigrant named Charles J. van Depoele had designed a rail-car that took power from an overhead wire. And in Baltimore Leo Daft had run a street locomotive draining power from an electrified third rail which, in a few months of operation, managed to electrocute one horse and a large number of dogs and chickens before the line went out of business.

Sprague's first electric car was far more sophisticated—though hardly more successful. In an attempt to sell the Manhattan Elevated Railway on electric traction, he designed a car powered by a pair of his constant-speed motors mounted on the truck and geared to the wheels. For smooth acceleration he designed a rheostat—a device that allowed progressively more current to flow to the motors as the car got under way. Even more important, he introduced a revolutionary concept called series-parallel controls which enabled the motors to make the most efficient use of that current as the car moved from a slow starting pace up to top speed. These three innovations, taken together, made possible the crucial breakthrough in urban rail transit technology—an arrangement which would, one day, run virtually all the world's subways, trolleys, elevated railways and electric-powered commuter trains.

Count me out

Full of confidence, Sprague invited the directors of the Manhattan elevated railway for a trial run, but unhappily he overplayed his hand before no less a person than Jay Gould, the main backer of the line, who was a visibly nervous passenger on the test run. "Keenly alive to the importance of our visitor," Sprague wrote many years later, "I suddenly reversed the motors and the instant excess rush of current blew the safety catch into a small volcano." Gould panicked and tried to jump off the moving car. Someone grabbed him; but at the end of the ride no one could convince the shaken financier that electricity was for the elevated railway. Sprague would have to score his first real success somewhere else.

That somewhere was Richmond, Virginia, where in May 1887 Sprague undertook to instal 12 miles of line and overhead wire, set up a 375-h.p. generating plant, build and equip 40 electric cars which could climb 8 per cent gradients—and operate the line for two subsequent months—all for a fee of £40,000. This was a tall order. At the time, there were in all the world no more than 19 electric street railways, operating fitfully over less than 60 miles of line, and fairly level line at that. Once again, Sprague seemed to have overreached. And, indeed, at first the work went badly. "The condition of the line was simply execrable," Sprague reported after an early inspection trip, "... poorly jointed, unevenly laid ... the foundation was red clay. The main curves were sharp, some with a 27-foot radius."

Worse yet, some of the gradients were as steep as 1 in 10, and Sprague was not at all sure his cars could make the climb. In a supposedly secret night trial, with Sprague and an assistant at the controls, a test car staggered to the crest of Richmond's steepest hill before a crowd of fascinated townspeople, the engine flaming hot, jerking badly for the last few yards.

"Unwilling to admit serious trouble," Sprague wrote years after, "I [said] in a tone that could be overheard, that there was some slight trouble in the circuits, and would [an assistant] go for the instruments. ... Then, turning out the light, I lay down on a seat to wait, while the crowd gradually dispersed. After waiting a long time [he returned] with those 'instruments' ... he came in sight with four of them—big powerful mules, the most effective aids which could be found in Richmond under the circumstances."

Jolly hour on the trolley

Back in the repair shed, Sprague and his partners raced against the contract's deadline, redesigning the gearing systems, rewinding the motor armatures. By some sort of minor miracle, they were ready to go by the end of January. "As a preliminary to regular operation," Sprague noted, "we spent a day carrying loads of children without any serious trouble, and about the 2nd of February, 1888, in a drizzling rain, we opened the line for regular service." The citizens of Richmond were dazzled. For about four pence a man could ride the entire 12 miles in the short space of an hour, at speeds up to 20 m.p.h. There was service every 10 minutes; the cars slid smoothly up the steepest gradient, and at night they were brilliantly lit by the new incandescent electric light bulbs.

Not long afterwards, in a special demonstration for the president of a Boston rail company, Sprague ran 22 electric cars simultaneously on one short stretch of line, clearing up any remaining doubts about the reliability of electric traction under heavy traffic. Boston promptly ordered 20 electric cars, and the rush among other cities to electrify was on. Within two years 200 trolley lines were running or being built, half of them using Sprague-built equipment and nearly all the others licensed to operate under his patents. Thirty years later, a total of some 70,000 cars were rolling over 43,000 miles of line carrying an annual load of 13,700,000,000 fares—more than any other form of public transport ever carried, before or since.

Though millions of American city dwellers were moving in his electric cars, Sprague was dissatisfied. He had a true genius's rankling notion that he had not designed those cars just right. Each trolley needed its own operator, and could be run only as a single car carrying no more

AN EARLY ELECTRIC CAR, developed by Frank Sprague, began test runs on New York City's Third Avenue Elevated Railway in 1886. The car rode on two trucks (one of which is seen below), each equipped with two small electric driving motors. Using current transmitted to the motors through a third rail, Sprague's electric car later evolved into the basic vehicles for fast and efficient city commuting—on elevated lines, ground-level railways and subways.

than 50 to 55 people. And each and every trolley was still running right down the middle of the ever-more-crowded city streets.

"The thought suddenly flashed on me," said Sprague, "why not . . . make a train unit by the combination of a number of individual cars, each complete [with motors and its own set of controls], and provide for operating them all simultaneously from any master switch on any car."

This apparently simple notion added up to a complete revolution in the application of power to urban transit—in fact, to all passenger rail travel of any kind. Instead of one locomotive pulling a string of powerless cars, now each car in the train would carry its own power system, would be, in effect, its own locomotive. With a string of self-propelled cars coupled together and operated by one set of master controls, a train of almost any length could start as quickly as a single trolley; there would be none of the wasteful business of a huge locomotive pulling one or two light cars during slack hours; and at the end of the line, the train could simply start back in the opposite direction, without the complicated point-switching procedures needed to get a conventional locomotive back up to the head of the train.

Sprague tried his idea on the directors of the South Side Elevated Railroad in Chicago, who decided to let him go ahead but first asked what guarantee Sprague could give that he would deliver.

Playing with trains

"No guarantee," replied Sprague, "except my past reputation and my prophecy that, if I get the contract, the manufacturing companies will be bidding on a subcontract for the motors within a fortnight." He got the contract, and Chicago got its cars. So disdainfully certain was Sprague of the simple excellence of his multiple-unit system that at the crucial trial runs, in July 1897, he turned over the controls to his 10-year-old son. And afterwards, in a high-spirited celebration, Sprague and his master mechanic Patrick O'Shaughnessy roared off in a string of cars at 30 m.p.h., happily coupling and uncoupling the cars on the run in a marvellous series of bangs and lurches.

By 1900 Boston and Brooklyn had also adopted Sprague's multiple-unit control system, to run elevated trains of five cars at top speeds of 25 m.p.h. with the ease of a single trolley car. Boston had already opened the first underground transit line in the U.S. with an electrified tunnel beneath Tremont Street. And the day was not far off when 1,500 million passengers each year would ride below the streets of Manhattan, 3,000 million in the London subway system, and millions of others around the world, all indebted to the genius of Frank Sprague.

While that day was approaching, however, there was one more violent change in the city, brought about by yet another new vehicle. The motorcar arrived, bringing with it almost unlimited personal mobility for each car owner, and touching off wave after wave of explosive growth in the physical size of the metropolis. The diameter of the urban mass ultimately jumped to 100—even 120—miles. Its area became 100 times as great as in 1800, and its population increased 100-fold and more. Furthermore, there was a dynamic shift in the distribution of that population. In both New York and Chicago, the number of people who actually lived in the centre reached its peak in 1910. But in the next 60 years the householders of these and other large cities moved outwards, riding on the swift wheels of the motor-car—and the bus—into the suburbs. By 1970, almost half the metropolitan population of the U.S. lived in suburbs. Businesses, or branches of businesses, soon followed.

A whole new pattern of settlement emerged, and with it, new patterns for traffic movement. Before World War I an American metropolis tended to look, from overhead, like a rimless wheel: the old central city was the hub, and the suburbs reached out like spokes along the railway and rapid-transit lines. By mid-century an interweaving of houses, highways and new towns began to fill up the gaps between the rails. The massive ebb and flow of city commuting and shopping trips was supplemented by travel to and fro in the suburbs themselves. So swift has been the growth that the suburbs of neighbouring cities have begun to overlap one another, creating a mammoth new urban phenomenon called the megalopolis, a kind of continuous super-city. There are six of these now alive or in gestation in the U.S., the largest of which stretches in an almost unbroken smear from Boston to Washington, D.C. Called the Northeast Corridor, it holds 20 per cent of the nation's population—and presents some new challenges in transportation.

Honk, screech and crash

But meanwhile the old central business district, the hub of each city within the megalopolis, is physically no larger than it was a century ago. The streets are still locked in the cramped grid pattern of the horse-drawn days. One-third of all U.S. motor trips grind along those streets, which still give easy access to roadside buildings but offer no relief whatever to the majority of drivers whose destination is somewhere on the other side of town. The buildings themselves, as residences and factories give way to commercial office buildings, add to the avalanche of traffic. In a city like Detroit, residential buildings in the centre generate only about 29 trips per acre per weekday, whereas an office building generates, on an average, 269. The larger the building, the more trips.

Despite the crush, and the energy crisis, motor-car traffic continues to proliferate. Once a man has tasted the solitary power and the door-to-door convenience of driving his own car, there seems no way of luring him on to a trolley, a commuter train, or even a bus. In the half century since the heyday of the trolley, the number of people riding on surface street railways has plummeted from 13,700,000,000 annually to less than 250 million. Half the defecting trolley riders switched to motor buses, which carry almost 70 per cent of the country's remaining transit riders, but even that business declined until the fuel shortage of 1973 and 1974 caused it to increase slightly. Since 1954, two hundred transit companies have gone out of business altogether.

In the cold light of logic, it is not surprising that the trolleys have died, that the elevated railways have been torn down, that the commuter railway trains are sinking fast. Old transportation methods will always give way to faster, more flexible ways of moving around. The problem is where to put all the cars and lorries, both *en route* and at their city destination. "It would undoubtedly be the ideal standard of travel", a transportation official in Chicago said, "if everyone were able, and could afford to execute all his movements in his own car, with complete safety, and deliver the car whenever the need for parking arose. But unless it is proposed that we first wreck from stem to stern the present pattern of city streets which we have inherited, we know that no such traffic Utopia is possible even if our national economy could afford it."

High-speed sardine cans

The most obvious solution—though not a very hopeful one—for the problem of moving people in and out of the city centre is to try and lure them back into an improved form of mass transit. This, at least, might ease some of the pressure of traffic. While a single lane on an expressway may handle 3,000 car passengers per hour, on that same lane a high-speed bus line can carry up to 20,000. And a single line of rail transit, running on tight schedules with only one and two minutes between trains— as on the London and New York subways—handles up to 50,000 in an hour. With these statistics in mind, Mexico City and Rotterdam recently dug into their soggy subsoils to provide commuters with enviably efficient subways. Munich, Montreal, Washington, D.C., and at least six other cities are currently extending old subways or establishing new ones. Meanwhile, in Philadelphia, the nation's first automated transit system, reaching $14\frac{1}{2}$ miles to Lindenwold, New Jersey, carries former car commuters to and from work in half the time they once spent. In Chicago, transit trains running along an eight-mile median strip on the Dan Ryan Expressway carry as many as 100,000 passengers a day. And Atlanta, after voting down a rapid-transit plan in 1969, approved a 1 per cent sales tax increase in 1971 to help pay for a 70-mile rapid rail and bus system scheduled for completion in 1980. Even Los Angeles, where the motor-car is king, hopes one day to get voter support for a plan that involves almost 100 miles of transit tracks.

These new mass transit facilities, supplementing a carefully planned network of highways, help to ease the crush—but only in the largest cities. All but a few of the urban centres where a subway is in operation or being built have populations of more than one million. For rail rapid transit, with its rigid routes and very low off-hour patronage which must be offset by a rich flow of customers during the rush hour, cannot survive without a heavy concentration of people, all with roughly similar demands for local transportation.

In smaller cities, the only practical kind of transit is the bus, whose flexibility in being able to stop at any street corner and change its route altogether with a mere turn of the wheel makes it far more useful for a growing, changing community than the current crop of rail-bound vehicles. In America, 5,000 million passengers now ride to work on buses. To speed schedules, such cities as Miami, Nashville, Baltimore and Dallas have set up systems of express buses during rush hours. In Dallas, downtown traffic lanes are reserved exclusively for these express buses, which carry 3½ million passengers a year.

All these plans for both bus and rail transit, however, amount to little more than minor technological alternatives which, like the horse-trams and trolley cars of the 19th century, may do little more in the long run than produce an even worse tangle in the city. "The time has already come", says G. Holmes Perkins in *The Future of Cities*, "when we are wasting our substance by attempting to squeeze more cars, goods, and people into smaller and smaller areas. The simple geometry of the plan will surely defeat us no matter how long we postpone the day by ingenious engineering. . . ."

Wisdom of the prophets

Something more fundamental than the simple engineering of better vehicles and the planning of high-capacity routes is needed. It is time to make a complete reassessment of the purpose of a city; and the design of a complete system of transportation to serve those needs. There must be a fresh understanding of the fact that a transportation network should be redesigned to serve the whole metropolitan complex—the suburbs and beyond as well as the central city—with a full complement of vehicles which can swiftly move masses of people to and fro on the fringes of the city, as well as in and out of the central business district. Even more important, the designers of the wheels for the city of the future must grasp the fundamental principle that traffic is not, basically, generated by highways and vehicles. Rather does it come from land use: certain types of land use generate far heavier traffic demands than others. The vehicles and roadways are merely a response to these demands. And therefore future cities must be built with the traffic potential of various land uses firmly in mind.

Finally, there must be a fresh consideration of the separate needs of vehicles and pedestrians. Stockholm has already put limits on motor traffic by closing off certain streets from 11 a.m. to midnight. And in London, an urban planner says, "No vehicle for individual transportation as we know it will be permitted in the so-called business area."

That sounds remarkably like Julius Caesar.

Said another, "There should be a pedestrian system of communications as efficient as that for the motor, and the less these two are provided in contiguity, the better for both".

Leonardo would think well of such a plan. In Washington, D.C., there was some serious talk about creating a system of green belts around the capital. Indeed it may turn out with cities, as it has with the men who built them, that the solution for the future lies in the lessons of the past —with a boost from the almost limitless power of new technology.

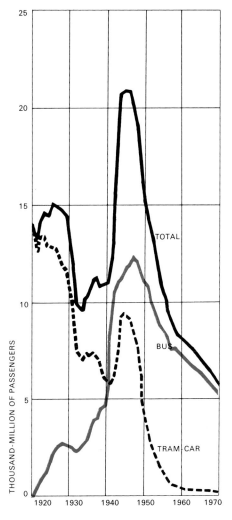

DECLINE OF THE TRAM-CAR since World War II is traced by the dotted line above. The use of buses (*blue line*) and tram-cars reached a peak in 1945, when their total patronage (*black line*) was 20,500 million. But with the end of the War and the disappearance of petrol rationing, the motor-car took over. By 1960 the number of bus riders had decreased to 7,100 million—in the decade following it continued dropping, to 5,000 million—and travel by tram-cars had all but faded from the picture.

Cities
without Congestion

In the fall of 1966 the Vice President of the United States, Hubert Humphrey, sold his house in Chevy Chase, Maryland, and bought an apartment near the U.S. Capitol. He had lived in the house for 18 years, and he liked it, but the nine-mile trip through Washington traffic to the Capitol took 40 minutes. Mrs. Humphrey complained that he seldom got home for dinner, and they had too little time together. So they moved. His new travel time: eight minutes.

Although Mr. Humphrey solved his problem, the frustrations that caused him to give up his house are still experienced by millions of city dwellers. In their cars they are trapped in traffic jams; if they try public transportation they fume over impossible connections. Eventually many of them simply give up living or working in the city and move away. Their wheels have failed them.

In scores of cities, however, something is being done about this paralysis. Rapid-transit, bus and rail terminals are being interconnected (*opposite*) for quick transfers. Expressways provide high-speed routes for long-distance traffic. And on the fringes of some cities, new towns are rising to bring urban attractions closer to the people who will use them.

A PLACID HUB OF TRANSPORTATION
The mall at Market East, a planned transportation complex in Philadelphia (*pages 160-161*), provides travellers with a place to walk unmolested by street traffic as they change from buses to trains or shop along the glass-roofed promenade. All modes of transportation are within a three-block area, but the mall runs seven blocks to City Hall (*background.*)

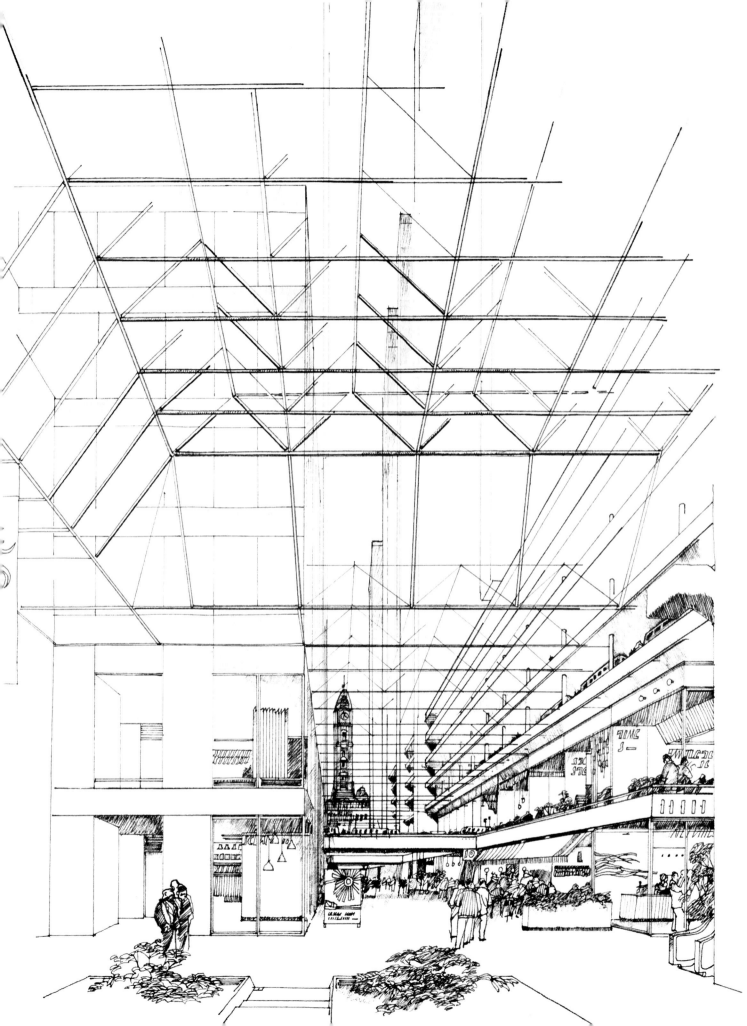

Easy Access by Expressway

The 18-mile drive from the suburb of Kenner to the heart of New Orleans used to take 45 minutes of twisting through lorry-clogged streets. Today, the six-lane Pontchartrain Expressway (*right*) and its connections enable cars to make the same trip in 20 minutes. This saving is achieved because the Pontchartrain, like the other superhighways built through and around scores of urban areas in the past 20 years, provides a route planned for speed: broad multiple lanes uninterrupted by traffic lights or crossings. This design depends on separating the traffic by keeping the through travellers away from the local ones. Yet in spite of these advantages, many city planners object to elevated expressways like the Pontchartrain. They feel that these high structures are great walls that tend to divide neighbourhoods and blight them with the noise of rushing traffic and darkness on the streets below. These planners prefer expressways at crossing levels, or below the ground, arrangements that leave neighbouring land useful for parks, blocks of flats or offices.

Besides speeding cars into and away from the city, expressways enable through travellers to stay out of the city entirely. Washington's new ring road, for example, circles the city proper, making it possible to go from Silver Spring, Maryland, to Alexandria, Virginia, on the other side of the metropolitan area, without ploughing through the centre of the city.

A ROAD TO THE CITY'S HEART
The Pontchartrain Expressway provides access to the centre of New Orleans for about 56,000 cars a day. It starts about five miles away as part of Interstate Highway 10, links here with Claiborne Avenue, a main road to the centre, and then continues to the river Mississippi bridge (*background*), bypassing the crowded city.

NEW ORLEANS BUSINESS SECTION

POYDRAS STREET

PONTCHARTRAIN EXPRESSWAY AND INTERSTATE 10

158

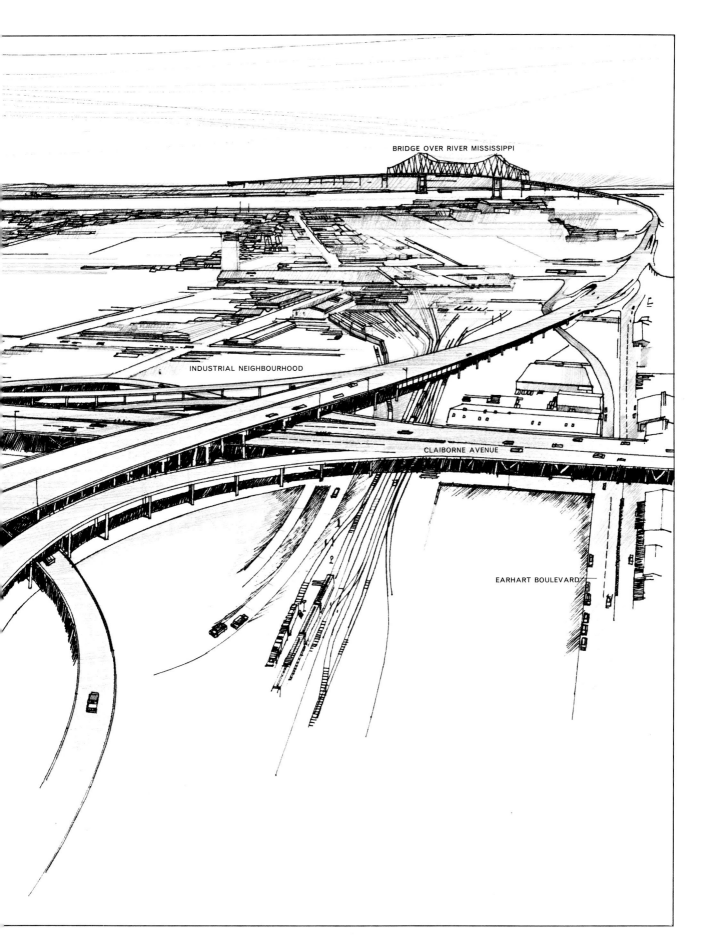

BRIDGE OVER RIVER MISSISSIPPI

INDUSTRIAL NEIGHBOURHOOD

CLAIBORNE AVENUE

EARHART BOULEVARD

159

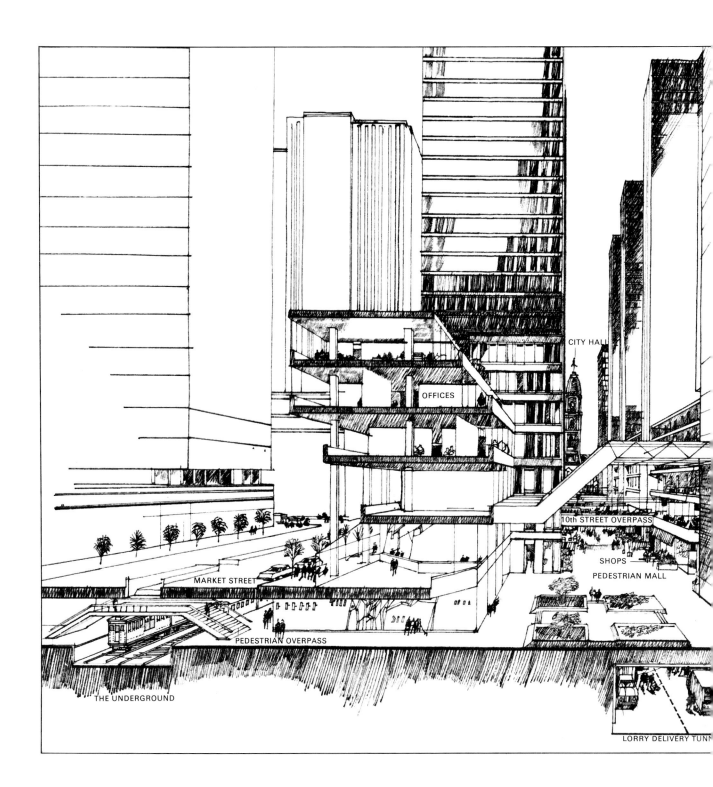

City Hall

OFFICES

10th STREET OVERPASS

SHOPS

PEDESTRIAN MALL

MARKET STREET

PEDESTRIAN OVERPASS

THE UNDERGROUND

LORRY DELIVERY TUNN

Philadelphia's Handy Interface

By 1990 a new transportation centre is scheduled to be built in Philadelphia. This project, Market East, is an example of what traffic engineers call an interface—a transfer point between different methods of transport. Lack of co-ordinated interfaces makes travel in or through a city a nightmare of lost time and missed connections; properly planned interfaces, such as Market East, simplify movement by organizing separate means of transport into an efficient system.

In Market East each kind of travel is to occupy a different level of the complex (*see drawing above*). At the far left is tree-lined Market Street, beneath which runs an underground railway, its three stations opening on to the broad, glass-enclosed pedes-

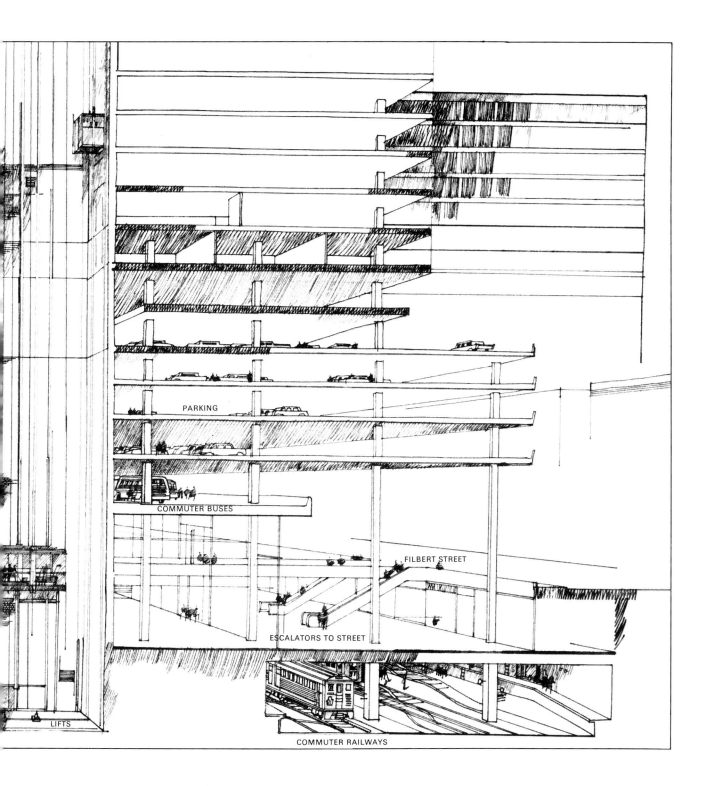

PARKING

COMMUTER BUSES

FILBERT STREET

ESCALATORS TO STREET

LIFTS

COMMUTER RAILWAYS

trian mall at the centre (*shown on page 157*). Below the mall is a tunnel for lorry deliveries, and to the right of this tunnel a commuter train station serves both the Reading and Penn Central Railroads. Bus terminals and a garage for 4,000 cars, originally planned to occupy space above the trains, as shown here, have since been moved across the street.

All these facilities will be interconnected by lifts, escalators and walkways leading to the mall, which is designed to serve two purposes. Not only will it link the various terminals but it will also carry pedestrian traffic to Market East's own buildings—an hotel, a library and possibly eight office structures, one of which would be 36 storeys high.

The Market-Place within Easy Reach

Traditionally, the chief attraction of the city has been its market-place, the central shopping district where the goods people need were brought together in an accessible position. But as the business area has become more congested, the market-place has moved out to its customers in a resplendent form, the suburban shop-

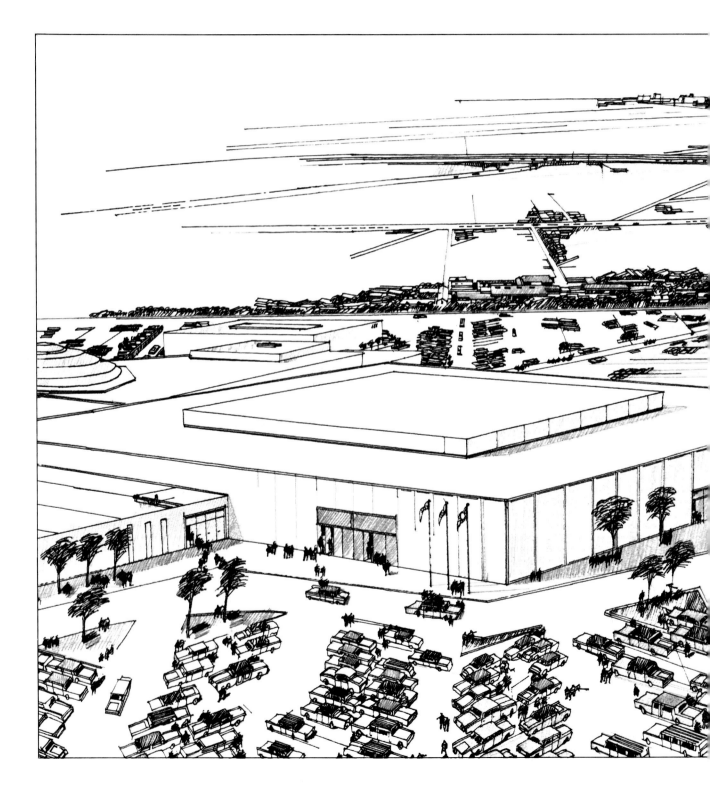

ping centre. In the one called Rand-hurst (*below*), 22 miles north-west of Chicago, 40,000 shoppers a day can sample the wares of three department stores and patronize some 80 shops and services, including a book shop, pet shop, ice rink and restaurant. All of these facilities, connected by show-window-lined promenades, are inside a huge air-conditioned building that covers 12 acres and has space for some 9,000 cars.

Such elaborate market-places are more than places to shop. Their au-ditoriums feature dramas, concerts and political debates; their prome-nades are often the scenes of dances and art shows. Some even have zoos for children to visit and pavement cafés for shoppers to enjoy. But these centres have now become the victims of congestion with resultant delays. Some cars must be parked as much as a quarter of a mile from the shopper's destination. In addition, traffic snarls frequently develop on the highways that feed in and out of the centres.

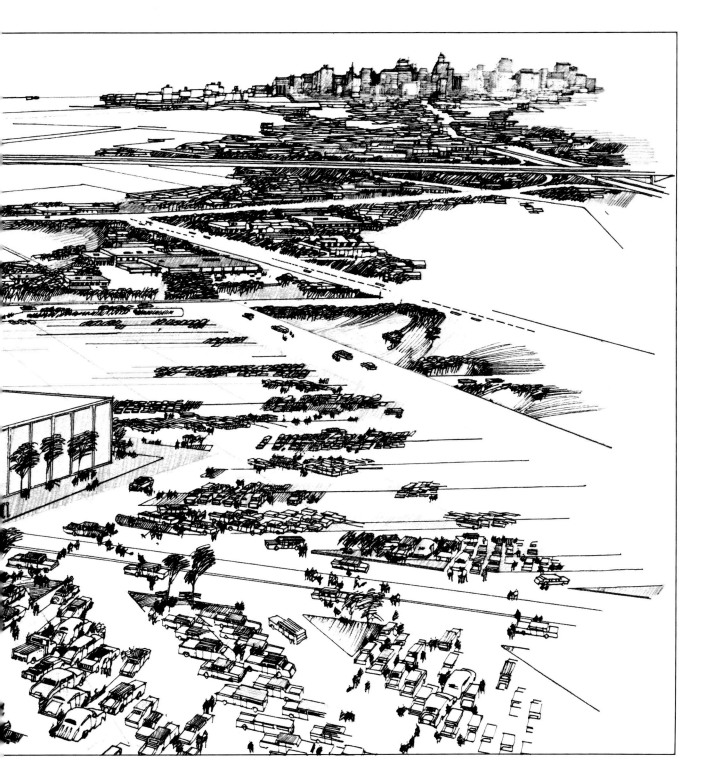

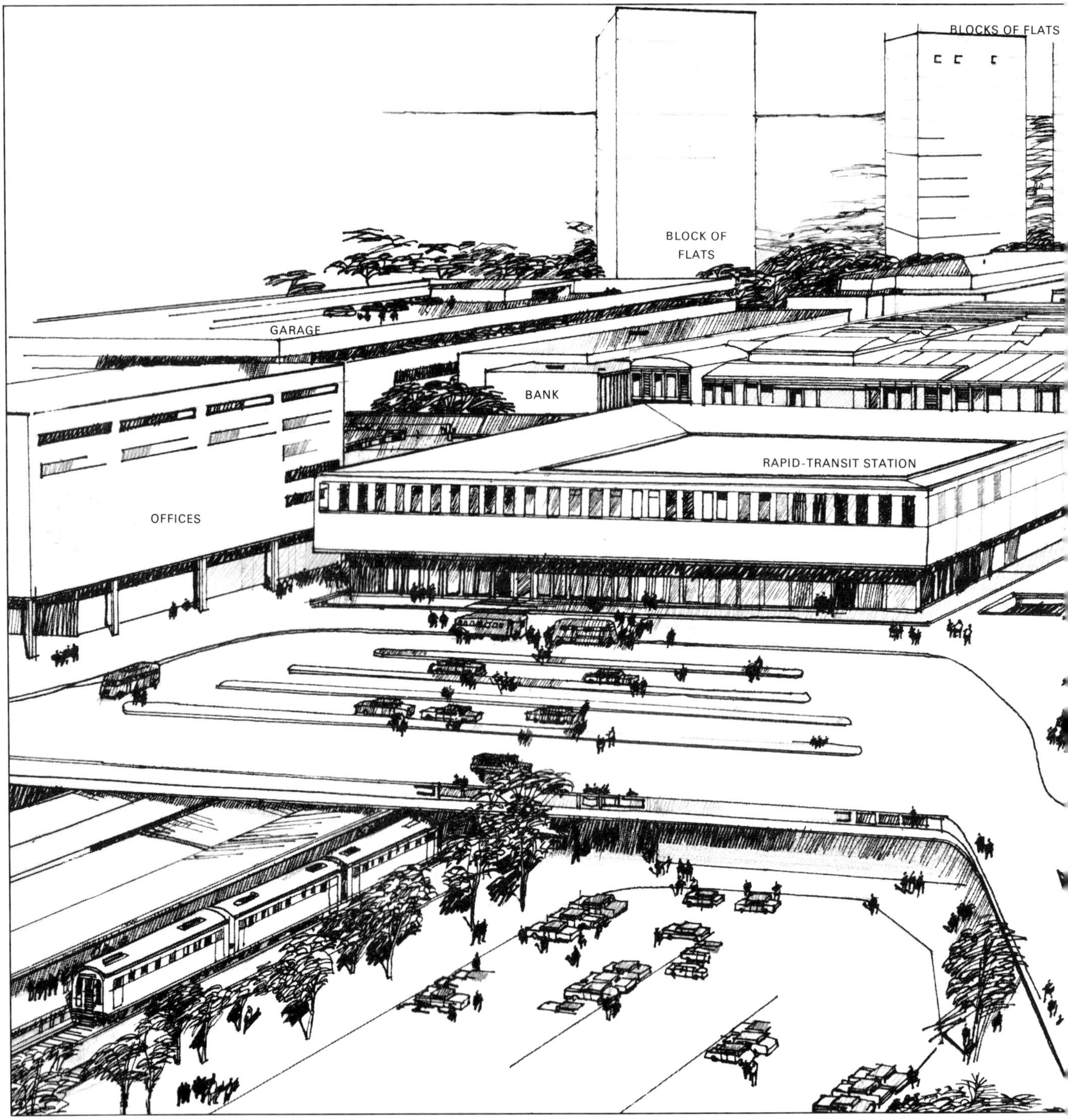
BLOCKS OF FLATS
BLOCK OF FLATS
GARAGE
BANK
RAPID-TRANSIT STATION
OFFICES

Satellite Cities in the Urban Orbit

On the outskirts of European metropolitan areas a new kind of city is being developed to reduce the need for travel. Called a "satellite city", the new community depends on the metropolitan core for some services, but offers within its own local area such a variety of urban attractions, ranging from offices to museums, that many residents seldom travel to the core. For those who do, the satellite provides direct, convenient public transportation.

Typical of these communities is Vallingby, Sweden, shown here. With 20,000 residents, it was the first of a series of satellite cities planned to ring Stockholm.

Vallingby is built on a rapid-transit line to Stockholm, nine miles from

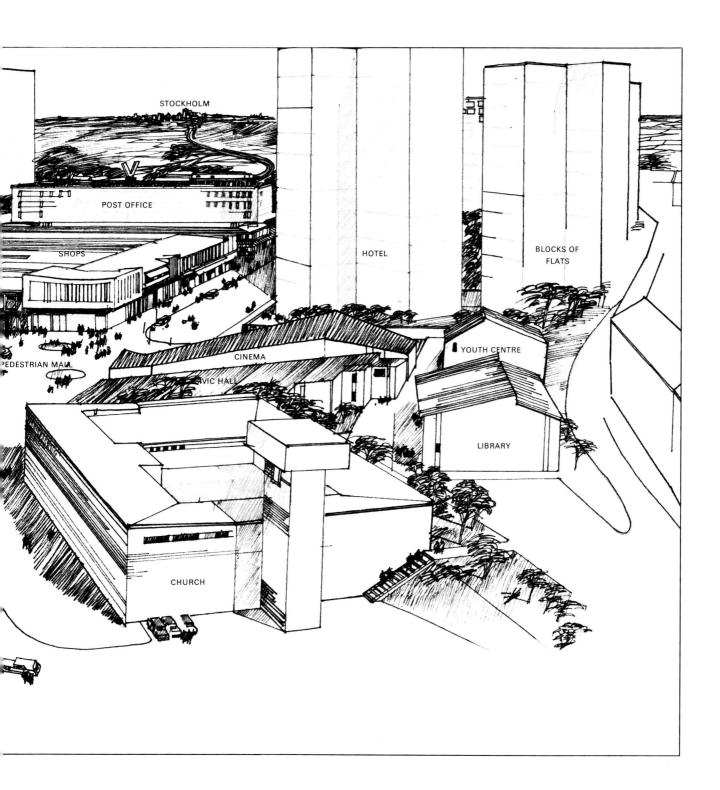

STOCKHOLM

POST OFFICE

SHOPS

HOTEL

BLOCKS OF
FLATS

PEDESTRIAN MALL

CINEMA

YOUTH CENTRE

CIVIC HALL

LIBRARY

CHURCH

the capital's core; the satellite's centre actually sits on a platform above the tracks. Clustered about the rapid-transit station are shops, a cinema, a civic hall, library, youth centre and church, all inter-connected by a pedestrian mall. In the background are tall blocks of flats arranged in groups; the Stockholm skyline is seen in the distance.

But Vallingby has demonstrated that even the best planning does not always work. Half its working population was expected to find employment with local businesses, but most of those jobs are filled, ironically, by people from neighbouring towns— while most of Vallingby's working residents commute to the centre of Stockholm and other near-by areas.

A New City in the Country

Columbia, Maryland, did not appear on any highway map in 1966. At that time its 13,690 acres of rolling green hills, 15 miles south-west of Baltimore, held only some construction machinery. But by 1980 Columbia will be a city of 120,000, a population that will make it the second largest in the State—and a model of a community that is planned for accessibility.

The city will be partitioned into seven villages, each centred on its own group of schools, churches and stores, so that facilities which everyone must use are often within walking distance of every home. The seven villages in turn will be clustered around the city core, which will contain less heavily used facilities—theatres, department stores, restaurants, a college and a glittering "Tivoli Gardens" for dining and entertainment. Moulding together this core and the villages will be a network of roadways. But cars will seldom be needed for local traffic, since plans call for Columbia to be served by a fleet of small, inexpensive buses. The drawing on the right shows how the city core is related to Wilde Lake, one of the villages. The two areas are linked directly together by an arterial roadway.

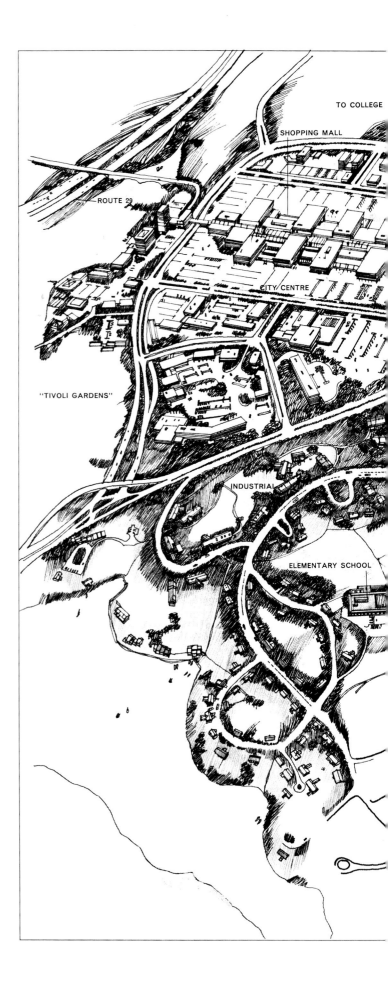

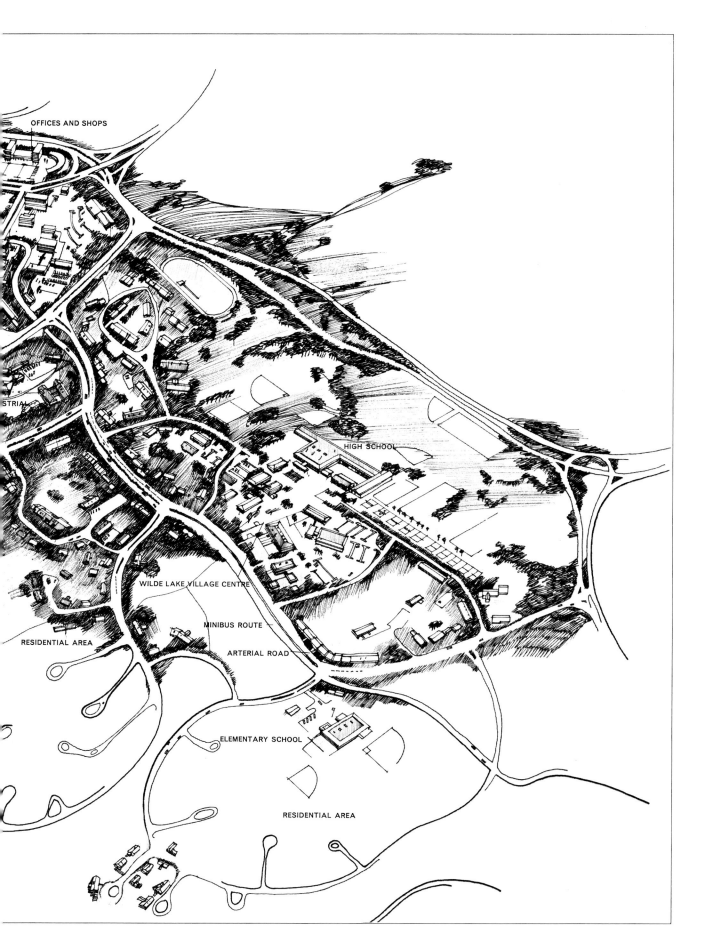

OFFICES AND SHOPS

STRIAL

HIGH SCHOOL

WILDE LAKE VILLAGE CENTRE

MINIBUS ROUTE

RESIDENTIAL AREA

ARTERIAL ROAD

ELEMENTARY SCHOOL

RESIDENTIAL AREA

167

8

The Automated Wheel

Monitoring the televised flow of cars from New York to New Jersey through the south tube of the Lincoln Tunnel, this traffic officer can direct the unsnarling of jams. In a rush hour, this section of the tunnel may handle 2,500 vehicles.

IT WAS THE NIGHT BEFORE CHRISTMAS, and the vice-president of an American greeting-card company was filled with cheer. He had just shipped off a big order: two goods wagons chock-full of Valentines, to a distributor who had asked for delivery the day after Christmas. But while the vice-president went joyfully home to his family, someone switched the wrong points. The goods wagons, like many thousands before them, rolled on to the wrong siding. There they sat for weeks, hopelessly lost, while a blizzard of protests whirled among the distributor, the railway and the now-cheerless shipper. Finally, the day after Valentine's Day, somebody found the wagons. What did the card company's vice-president do with the Valentines? "We ate them", he said, grimly, and he was not the only man who munched on lost freight that winter.

In Detroit, the president of one of the largest U.S. highway delivery firms talked about some of his special problems in land transportation. "The cities kill us", he said. "New York is murder. It takes for ever to get a truck in and out—the traffic, parking, unloading, pilferage, the whole works. You kill a whole day. They ought to have one big terminal across the river and move the freight in on conveyor belts."

In New Shrewsbury, New Jersey, a businessman was planning a return trip to Cambridge, Massachusetts, 220 miles away. Most of those miles were to be covered in a 600-m.p.h. jet in about 30 minutes. But by the time he had driven to the bus stop, changed to the airport limousine, walked, waited, and climbed in and out of traffic-stalled taxis, he had used up four hours going and four hours coming back. The day was shot, and his average speed for the trip was 55 m.p.h.—7 m.p.h. below that attained over a measured mile by Mile-A-Minute Murphy on his bicycle in 1899.

All across the nation the wheels of land transportation were still turning too slowly. And these three men, along with millions of other Americans, were losing time, money and patience through their slowness. The sluggish pace was no fault of the wheels themselves. Under the right conditions a modern train can move as fast as any train may ever need to go: between Bordeaux and Dax, France, in 1955, two electric locomotives went howling down the track at 205.6 m.p.h. The speeds of motor vehicles are even more impressive. In 1965 on the Utah Salt Flats, Craig Breedlove, clinging to the controls and praying for the tyres of his jet speedster, became the first driver to go over 600 m.p.h.

It will be some time before anyone wants to transport himself or his products overland as fast as this. The trouble is that the right conditions have not yet been provided on the public thoroughfares for even a fraction of this speed. On an uneven, traffic-clogged right-of-way, a train or car capable of 100 m.p.h. rattles along at average speeds of 10 to 45 m.p.h. At the terminals, there are not enough quick ways to transfer goods and people from one kind of wheel to another. Each different line of vehicular technology—railways, motor-cars, tram-cars, subways, buses, lorries, and the roads, bridges and tunnels which carry them—has evolved separately, in response to separate, short-range developments. As each one was designed, there was no thought—and, in fairness, no early evidence—that they would one day all run together in a quarrelsome, inefficient tangle. Nor did anyone realize that the wheels would become as much the shapers of the community as the servants of it.

As a result of this haphazard development, today's society not only requires a system of transportation that would integrate all the different kinds of wheels but also one that would radically change the layouts of cities and suburbs—and even the conduct of activities within them.

Space Age wheels

But society's demand for mobility cannot wait for cities to be redesigned and the habits of generations to be overturned. Some quick steps must be taken to speed up the shambling pace of the existing land-transportation machinery; and the first of these steps is already being made by adapting Space Age technology to conventional means of transport. One of the most valuable innovations is the automation of railway traffic control, which the roads are swiftly adopting to monitor inter-city goods movement that may multiply two and a half times in volume by the year 2000. This control can be so precise that today, on the Southern Railway, for example, a lost car full of Valentines—or anything else—is a near impossibility.

Several years ago, tough-talking, fast-moving Bill Brosnan, then president of Southern, set out to create the most advanced system of traffic anywhere in the world. He hired retired Air Force Colonel George W. Thorpe, one of the designers of the control room for the world-wide network of Strategic Air Command bases and bombers. "SAC has about the same number of bases as the Southern has terminals," said Thorpe. "SAC's inventory at each base moves around, needs maintenance, and moves on exact schedules. So do Southern trains." Beginning with this concept and building outwards from an IBM 705 computer, the Southern proceeded to erect a highly computerized system of control. The operations centre, located in Atlanta, looks like a war room. Some 30 desks range over three terraces of linoleumed floor facing a 12- by 15-foot wall chart of Southern's 11,000-mile rail network. In the middle of the top terrace sits a spooky-looking "cage", a raised cubicle enclosed with tinted green glass, where the men most responsible for keeping the railway moving work at desks stacked with their daily supply of computer read-outs and Xeroxed station records.

The data they use come from Southern's five automated goods yards, where batteries of TV cameras scan the numbers on the sides of cars moving in and out. When a dispatcher sends off a train, he calls operations control on the railway's private microwave radio network to report the train and engine numbers, the sum total of loaded cars versus empty ones, and the time the train arrived in the yard as well as the time of departure. Somewhat later, he feeds into his long-distance Xerography sender the detailed information that appears on each car's waybill, including its number, load and destination. When this information comes out of the receiving machines on continuously moving rolls at Southern's

WORLD LAND SPEED RECORDS

DATE	DRIVER	CAR	MPH
1898	CHASSELOUP-LAUBAT	LA JAMAIS CONTENTE	39.24
1899	CHASSELOUP-LAUBAT	LA JAMAIS CONTENTE	57.60
1904	RIGOLLY	GOBRON-BRILLIE	103.56
1925	M. CAMPBELL	BLUEBIRD	150.87
1927	SEGRAVE	SUNBEAM	203.79
1932	M. CAMPBELL	BLUEBIRD	253.97
1935	M. CAMPBELL	BLUEBIRD	301.13
1938	COBB	RAILTON	350.20
1964	D. CAMPBELL	BLUEBIRD	403.1
1964	A. ARFONS	GREEN MONSTER	434.02
1964	BREEDLOVE	SPIRIT OF AMERICA	526.28
1965	BREEDLOVE	SPIRIT OF AMERICA	555.127
1965	A. ARFONS	GREEN MONSTER	576.553
1965	BREEDLOVE	SPIRIT OF AMERICA	600.601
1970	GABELICH	BLUE FLAME	622.407

CHAMPION SPEEDSTERS, the cars and drivers listed above each established a new world land speed record. The first two records were set in an electric car. Piston engines then ruled the speed trials until Donald Campbell's jet-powered *Bluebird* set a new record in 1964. Then two jet-powered vehicles—Craig Breedlove's *Spirit of America* and Art Arfons's *Green Monster*—began a see-sawing duel for the land speed mark, only to be surpassed in 1970 by Gary Gabelich in his *Blue Flame* rocket car.

computer centre, it is fed into a computer while copies are distributed to the men working in the cage.

If someone in the operations centre wants to know the whereabouts of one of the company's 75,000 cars, he punches the car number on a keyboard that is connected to the computer. Instantaneously a machine prints out an answer, telling him where that car was located a few hours earlier. Whether or not the car will be delayed can be ascertained by a glance at the wall chart, where large red arrows mark traffic tie-ups. Should a customer inquire about his Valentines, Southern could track them down in seconds.

Keeping track of 175,000 goods wagons

Not to be outdone, the Penn Central claims its computer system can locate any of its 175,000 goods wagons over some 20,000 miles of track in about one-fifth of a second. To get the goods moving still faster, the Penn Central and other pioneering lines are completely automating the sorting and switching of trains in their yards. At the Penn Central's Conway Yard (*pages 74, 75*), such automation has helped cut goods travel time from Pittsburgh to the Mississippi to a fast 21 hours. The Southern Pacific's West Colton, California yard—the most highly automated railway yard in the United States—can switch and mix trains at the rate of 6 to 8 per minute.

Along with automated traffic handling, the railways have added some ingenious ways of carrying goods. Instead of the traditional practice of making up a goods train with a mixed bag of different cars, many of them with different final destinations, the railways are now turning more and more to the relatively new "unit" trains, identical strings of 100 or more identical coaches, shuttling between two fixed terminals. These unit trains, travelling at speeds of 60 to 70 m.p.h. behind powerful new locomotives, add a whole new dimension in mobility to industrial production. At Bethlehem Steel's Lackawanna, New York, plant, hot steel slabs roll on to unit-train flat-trucks and are fed, still warm, to a Bethlehem rolling mill in Burns Harbor, Indiana, 500 miles away. Another unit train rolls out of Detroit carrying 1,800 brand-new motor-cars on triple-decker rack trucks for delivery 24 hours later at Atlantic terminals. And on the Louisville and Nashville, as well as some 20 other rail lines, unit trains of hopper trucks haul as much as 10,000 tons of coal from mineheads to electricity utility plants, where the cars are automatically dumped either by giant tumblers which flip them over bodily, or by blasts of compressed air which trips the doors while the trains are still moving.

Perhaps the most significant rail innovation of all—since it represents the first real blending of railways with another major mode of land transportation—carries the modest name of "pick-a-back". Its beginning was correspondingly modest. "Just before a rainy midnight in 1954," reads a Penn Central report, "a fast through freight to Chicago pulled away from the fog-filled Meadows Yard in the marshlands of New Jersey with half a dozen [highway] truck trailers secured pick-a-back fashion to flatcars." Each of those truck trailers had picked up its cargo at the shipper's door and delivered it by fast, flexible highway service to the rail terminal. Now the trailers, with their tractors unhitched, were heading for a distant destination, riding on the long-distance economy of rails. Two decades after that rainy night, one 12-month period saw more than 2.6 million highway trailers riding pick-a-back fashion instead of rolling along on crowded roads. "The final impact of pick-a-back," said one railman, "is nowhere in sight." Even so, railways have made some predictions, and one forward-looking company expects pick-a-back to account for as much as 20 per cent of its total traffic.

The all-purpose container

By the 1970's, a more sophisticated form of pick-a-back, called containerization, was making the service more efficient and useful. In transportation terms, a container is a sealed storage unit of standard size up to 8 by 8 by 40 feet, containing any kind of freight and able to ride on any major form of transportation without altering, opening or re-packing (*pages 184, 185*). "The two steel rails give railways unquestionable superiority in providing high-speed, long-distance transportation," said the late Morris Forgash, then president of America's largest freight-forwarding operation, the United States Freight Company. "That, combined with the flexibility, manœuvrability and economic advantages of lorries as short-distance carriers, gives you true co-ordination." Going forward still another step, scores of ocean-going merchant ships are being built or altered to receive containers, and jet-powered cargo planes, as well as jumbo passenger jets, are carrying containerized freight to all parts of the world.

Thus, by making full, imaginative use of the best of existing technology, the container concept has created the focal point for a working model of the freight-handling system of the future. In this scheme a cargo of sealed containers rolls by conveyor belt from the hold of a merchant ship to the flat wagons of a unit train. The loaded train moves off through an automated yard behind a computer-controlled robot electric locomotive. In 24 hours the cargo has travelled 800 miles by rail, say, from a dock at Baltimore to a classification yard in Chicago. There the containers are again switched to lorries and cargo planes for "same-day" delivery to customers scattered over half a dozen States.

In the handling of passenger traffic, too, there are some green shoots of technological progress. In San Francisco, the new urban rail transit system called the Bay Area Rapid Transit (BART for short) is equipped with carpeted electric cars that are remotely controlled by computers to travel at speeds up to 80 m.p.h. BART provides service to 33 stations in three counties and is designed to carry 160,000 passengers a day. Its 71-mile route, almost evenly divided into surface, elevated and subway track, includes a 3.6-mile-long transbay tube that connects San Francisco with the East Bay area.

Despite delays in the completion of its system and early problems with the operation of the computerized controls, BART has pointed the way for other high-speed urban transit projects. The concept of mass transit has become more popular as public concern about energy shortages and the environment has increased. But before BART or any other new transit system has time to make any significant change in people's travel habits, the number of motor-cars in the United States will increase to at least 120 million. In one last effort to keep the wheels rolling—rather than legislating most of them out of town as Stockholm is doing—U.S. highway engineers are turning to railway-inspired automatic traffic controls. In Chicago a computer, behaving very much like those in the Southern Railway's control room, keeps count of the vehicles on the 6.5 miles of Eisenhower Expressway through electronic detectors positioned along the highway. When heavy traffic begins to clog the Expressway during rush hours, signals regulate the inflow from entrance ramps. Red lights there turn green just long enough to release one car at a time into the Expressway stream, the frequency of release being controlled by a computer that gauges how many more cars the Expressway can absorb.

Computers instead of "cops"

In Baltimore computers direct almost all of the city's traffic lights, getting their vehicle counts from radar detectors that hang over streets. The computers judge the flow of converging traffic at 850 intersections, and alter the timing of the lights to give longer green signals to the street with the heaviest load. "It was found," said the late Henry Barnes, traffic commissioner in Baltimore and later traffic tsar in New York, "that on many streets the volume of vehicles per lane per hour was increased from about 450 vehicles . . . to as high as 1,200 vehicles. Yet the driving time from point A to point B was reduced to one-third of what it had been with only 450 vehicles in the lane."

Barnes introduced a similar system in New York to handle 2,700 intersections. In Toronto a Univac 1107 tells 500 traffic lights what to do, not only controlling ordinary traffic flow but shutting off streets blocked by fires or accidents, and providing especially long green signals for Saturday night hockey crowds. Even the Univac, however, is sometimes stumped by a traffic tangle; at such moments it hammers out the word "Please" on its print-out.

Burrowing deep down towards the fundamental causes of traffic problems, engineers have collaborated with physicists to apply laws of fluid dynamics to the mass movement of motor vehicles. In Düsseldorf, Germany, engineers discovered that traffic moves more swiftly in regulated platoons than in a solid stream. In the flow of normal traffic a slowdown by a single driver in a long line will travel back through the line in a series of shock waves, sometimes bringing vehicles miles down the road to a complete stop. When the traffic is divided into platoons, however, these shock waves are absorbed by the open spaces between platoons, and 5 to 15 per cent more cars can move per hour over a given stretch with no tie-ups. To keep the vehicles in orderly platoons, the German

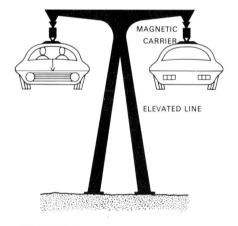

SUSPENDED CARS, hung from elevated lines, could provide safe inter-city travel at about 120 m.p.h. in a futuristic system proposed by Robert A. Wolf of Cornell Aeronautical Laboratories. Each car would be attached magnetically to a carrier that would be guided by a rail, driven by an electric motor and accelerated or braked by a central computer. This automatic steering and control, protecting against accidents, would leave the driver free to enjoy scenery, or even to sleep, until he reached his exit. There, lowered to the ground and released from the carrier, he would drive over city streets to his destination.

engineers programmed a computer to vary road-speed signs and the red-green cycles of traffic lights.

Detroit, too, is beginning to produce new ideas for vehicular control. Perhaps the most significant, since it leads directly towards an automated system for handling passenger traffic, is General Motors' experimental car that runs by itself. Working with RCA, GM engineers installed a computer system in one of their cars and hooked the system to electrohydraulic controls on the throttle, brakes and front wheels. Beneath a test track at Princeton, New Jersey, they laid a cable which generated an electromagnetic field. On the front of the car were four magnetically sensitive coils connected to the computers. Once the test car was positioned over the guiding cable, the vehicle began to roll, its speed set by impulses from the cable. If the car began to drift off the cable's path, the sensing coils transmitted the error to the computer, which corrected the steering. If the vehicle got too close behind another test car, the robot car slowed down until safe spacing was again established. At any time, a front-seat passenger in the robot car had the option of switching to manual controls and passing the car ahead.

100 m.p.h. with no hands

Here again, using only existing technology and equipment, the U.S. has the bare bones of a highway passenger system of the future. A commuter heading for the office 55 miles away pulls out of his drive with his car under manual control. He manœuvres three miles through local streets to the entrance ramp of a superhighway whose inside lanes are wired for automatic speed and spacing control. Traffic lights responding to computer instructions admit his car to the highway. Quickly he pushes the speedometer up to 100 m.p.h., moves to the centre lane, switches to automatic control, and sits back to enjoy the morning paper in the privacy of his own highway club car. Half an hour later, in response to a warning buzz, he switches back to manual, takes his exit cue from another set of computer-controlled lights, and rolls off the highway on to the street leading to his office. Total elapsed time: about 45 minutes, with the convenience at each end of a personal vehicle, and the mid-route efficiency of fast, safe, train-type travel.

As promising and technologically sound as this concept may be, however, it can never come to pass until the yawning chasm between motor-car builders and highway builders is amicably closed. Until now, like other branches of the transportation industry, each has gone its own way with too little regard for the goals of the other—not to mention the real desires of the public which this transportation is supposed to serve. "What we really need", said one car executive, "is a proper system of guideways which will permit us to run cars and other land vehicles to their full potential". Said another car man, "The rail people are far better off in this thing than we are. They can control the vehicle and the road and the terminal. It's all theirs. All we can do, really, is make the car. And maybe the highway people want to do something we don't agree with. We don't control them, and we darn sure don't control the railroads."

In fact, the only people who can exercise any wide measure of control over all types of wheeled vehicles are federal officials in Washington—and by the 1960's they had become aware of the need for a fully integrated system of land transport. In 1965 President Johnson signed into law a bill calling for £35 million to finance research on new methods of high-speed overland travel in the Washington-to-Boston megalopolis called the Northeast Corridor. The bill complemented another signed a year earlier earmarking £280 million for urban mass transit. These two programmes were scarcely launched when Congress approved the creation of a Cabinet-level Department of Transportation, whose functions included improving land travel—using available equipment—and investigating entirely new vehicles for the future. To finance the work this mandate required, Congress in 1970 passed the Urban Mass Transportation Assistance Act, which committed £3,900 million to be spent over 12 years. The cause of balanced transportation received a second boost that year when the government established a quasi-public corporation, called Amtrak, to operate—and keep alive—the nation's decaying rail passenger service.

Automated trains—and the "right mix"

One of the government's earliest moves in the mass transit field was to pump money into the final phase of San Francisco's BART project, some of it for development of the automated train controls that regulate speed and maintain safe headway. In the East, other seed money, from the Government's Northeast Corridor project, went towards the Pennsylvania Railroad's purchase of 50 luxurious self-propelled electric railway coaches that can cruise at 110 m.p.h. over welded rails—and cut rail travel time from New York to Washington from 3 hours 55 minutes to 2 hours 59 minutes. Similar funds have gone to the New Haven Railroad for 160 m.p.h. gas-turbine cars that operate out of Boston.

Such demonstrations are intended, said Robert Nelson of the Northeast Corridor project, "to determine whether the rail passenger system of the U.S. has economic utility. By providing high speeds and some of the amenities—like phones and TV and stewardesses—can we get people out of their cars and into public transportation?"

Said another transportation expert, "This is not primarily a matter, as it is so often put in popular discussion, of 'rail versus rubber', but rather a question of determining the right mix of the means available." The "right mix" may include a vastly increased use of air transport, particularly transit helicopters, which already carry more than a million Americans each year, and the still-experimental VTOL (Vertical Take-Off and Landing) aircraft, which can rise vertically like a helicopter, then level off for 300-m.p.h.-plus flight like a jet. The right mix will be a combination of not just the best and fastest in new transport technology, but that combination which makes cash sense to the riding public. Thus the crucial equation in transport today, just as it was in 1804 when Rich-

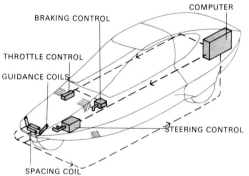

AN ELECTRONIC CAR, developed by General Motors and RCA, may one day speed down special roads while its owner leaves the driving to a computer. The car straddles a buried road cable that transmits signals to four coils behind the front bumper. Two of these coils sense right-and-left distance from the road cable and send signals (*dotted line*) to the computer to adjust the steering, keeping the car on course. The other two coils gauge the distance to the next car ahead and tell how fast it is travelling: with these data the computer can calculate a safe speed, set the throttle appropriately and, if necessary, apply the brakes.

ard Trevithick ran the world's first railway locomotive, is the cost of the technology versus the value of the service it provides. Robert Nelson, the Northeast Corridor project's first administrator, stated the case succinctly. "We have three basic problems. Number one is economics. The economics of speed are acute. Craig Breedlove can go 600 m.p.h. on the Utah Salt Flats; but it's too expensive. We know that technology can make any kind of vehicle we want right now. The trick is to get the one that makes economic sense."

Inter-city subway at 400 m.p.h.

As a first step towards solving the economics of speed, the U.S. government let out a series of research contracts to M.I.T., Cornell and other centres where engineers pulled out and picked over a lot of pet ideas that had been lying around for years—in addition to some wholly new concepts. One is a 400-m.p.h. inter-city subway. It would be driven by jet engines, or sucked by vacuum, through a tight-fitting tube in which the vehicle might support itself not on wheels, but on the air pressure its passage creates along the walls of the guideway. Other slightly less futuristic possibilities include a steel-wheeled vehicle that is propelled—at speeds up to 250 m.p.h.—by electromagnetism between the vehicle and an aluminium rail in the centre of the guideway, and a 300-m.p.h. vehicle that moves on a cushion of air over a central track, either propelled electrically or powered by a jet engine. Desirable as these advanced vehicles might be for their speed, even they have an inherent shortcoming: not one can function in any system not specifically designed for it.

This brings the search for a high-speed ground system squarely up against its second major problem: what transportation experts call the "interface". This is the terminal, or exchange point, where different modes of transportation come together—or fall apart, as the case may be. A horrible example of an interface is any urban air, bus or train terminal where that frustrated traveller from New Shrewsbury, New Jersey, to Cambridge, Massachusetts, can fumble away four hours of an eight-hour round trip. An example of a good interface is the new Schipol Airport in Amsterdam. The Schipol terminal building is set right on top of layers of highways and car parks next to bus, train and rapid-transit facilities, so that an air traveller can transfer immediately to any other transport mode he needs. The design, location and construction of these interfaces is crucial. "Particularly in urban areas", says Charles Miller, head of the Urban Systems Laboratory at Massachusetts Institute of Technology, "you can develop an exotic vehicle, but it will never be a commercial success because of the costs of the terminals."

In all the experiments, there is one strain of exotic vehicles which seems likely to survive and prosper, partly because it eliminates the need for terminals. These are the so-called bimodal vehicles which, like General Motors' experimental robot car, can operate individually as a single, manually controlled car for local use, but can also operate in a group flowing into an automated highway train for long-distance, high-

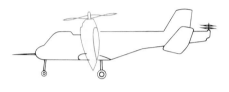
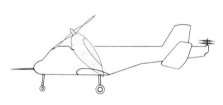

A DOUBLE-DUTY AIRCRAFT, the VTOL (Vertical Take-Off and Landing) can fly both vertically and horizontally to carry passengers from city centre to city centre. At take-off (*top*), the wings of the VTOL point skywards and the plane lifts off like a helicopter. As it gains altitude, the wings begin to level (*centre*) until they reach normal position (*bottom*) and the plane flies horizontally at jet speeds. Combining high speed with the ability to use small landing spaces, the VTOL may soon ease travel in crowded areas.

speed, mass travel. The more advanced designs come by various names —such as Urbomobile, Commucar, StaRRcar. In detail these vehicles vary only as to how many people they carry—some are minibuses, others are individual cars—whether they are powered by petrol or by electricity and whether on the highway they couple together magnetically or maintain tight intervals by remote control. And all of them are designed to run on an automated, computerized highway.

Making the wheels of the future roll

The third problem, and perhaps the most crucial of all in designing a transportation system, is working out what people want. For the moment, they seem to want the privacy and the flexible performance of the motor-car. In fact, it is quite possible that the inherent advantages of the motor-car—and the car owner's stubborn preference for it—could cause systems concepts to fall short of their theoretical potential. If this happens, other systems must be swiftly developed before each line of vehicular technology, moving independently as it always has, helps to create such a tangle of roadways and a plethora of machines that all our wonderful wheels come grinding to a halt.

In seeking the answer, the most crucial fact for all the researchers and government officials to remember is this: the so-called transportation problem is only half a transportation problem. Half the problem is to supply the facilities for moving. The other half is to create an environment in which the transportation system has a chance to work. This does not just mean designing faster vehicles and automated guideways. It means, perhaps, a complete rearrangement of our patterns of living (*pages 157-166*).

For the fact is that all over the world, both in urban areas and rural areas, the land is badly used. The wrong buildings, the wrong activities, the wrong outlets for human aspiration are placed too close to one another—or too far apart. The result is an unnatural demand for transportation, and an unnatural way of living. The men who design for the future must think first how people want to live—not just in the U.S., but in the emerging nations, too, where there is a superb opportunity to create balanced communities without first having to tear down great piles of misplaced steel and concrete. Then, and only then, can the technologists build a system of transportation to serve that way of life.

Whatever they decide, however they build that system, it seems certain that the builders will lean heavily on one old ally whose simple strength and superb utility has survived since the Age of Bronze. In a recent research project, an engineer at Lockheed Aircraft sought the ideal system for guidance and suspension in a high-speed land vehicle. He assembled pounds of research, scoured 100 years of patent literature, weighed reams of data on friction, speed variation, reliability, load-carrying capacity, manufacturing and maintenance costs, stability, rolling resistance. And after a suitable period he produced a description of the finest conceivable instrument. It is called a wheel.

Tomorrow's Vehicles

In London, in Washington, D.C., and in Boston, Detroit, and a dozen other transportation centres, research teams are taking up the challenge of travel delays, freight bottle-necks and traffic tangles. Their goal is a co-ordinated transport system—a combination of new vehicles and methods which will meet the problems modern society encounters in moving its people and its goods. Already the elements needed to build that integrated system are beginning to take shape. Long-haul lorries may exploit the concentrated power of smoothly spinning gas turbines. With conventional trains taking advantage of better road-beds and computer control systems, and new hybrids travelling on a cushion of air like the experimental vehicle at right, rail schedules may one day rival the speed and efficiency of airlines, as they now do in Japan.

As a first step in putting together a co-ordinated system, the research teams have adapted new power units and controls to some of the best of the existing equipment. The result is a breed of vehicles so promising that many of them have been hustled into regular service. In fact, a fair portion of the future technology of the wheel is already here, and many of tomorrow's vehicles are carrying the world's commerce today.

FLOATING DOWN THE RAIL
Jet-powered trains, like this research vehicle being tested at the U.S. Department of Transportation's High Speed Ground Test Centre, Pueblo, Colorado, may move at aeroplane speeds. The jets supply the compressed air to lift the craft off the guideway and keep it centred between the side rails. Electric current in the rails and in the vehicle propels the train.

Hovering hybrids for land and water

The machines on this page are samples of the remarkable ways in which a radical new vehicular principle can be put to work. They have no wheels but float on a cushion of air. Some of these air-cushion vehicles (ACVs), like the British Hovercraft on the right, skim over water and glide up or down a landing platform. Others, like the French Aerotrain below, use the air cushion to guide them along fixed tracks. Still others are designed to navigate swamps and marshes.

The Aerotrain is one of several experimental trains that employ the ACV idea. Straddling a centre guideway rail, it is lifted and guided by air pressurized by electric compressors: air forced down raises the vehicle just above the smooth track, while air blown against both sides of the central rail guides it.

Already in commercial use for over-water travel are a number of ACVs, which simply keep a bubble of pressurized air beneath their hulls. First developed by Great Britain in 1953, they operate in the English Channel and in a dozen countries. The U.S. Navy deployed similar vehicles in Vietnam. More than a dozen U.S. companies produce air-cushion vehicles and many more are testing them.

SKIMMING THE CHANNEL
Its propellers whirring (*above*), a gas-turbined air-cushion vehicle sends up a cloud of spray on its half-hour trip across the English Channel between Dover and Boulogne. One of two operated by British Rail Hovercraft, the craft is powered by four turbines of 3,400 h.p. each. It has a crew of 15 and carries 254 passengers and 30 vehicles at cruising speeds of 55 knots (57 m.p.h.). The vehicles operate on a regular schedule: 12 a day during spring and summer months, four or five a day off season. At journey's end (*below*) rear doors open to disgorge vehicles.

FLYING ABOVE A TRACK
The Aerotrain (*left*), shown from the rear, floats five-eighths inch above a three-foot high centre guideway on its 12-mile track at Chevilly, France. A more advanced version of this demonstration vehicle that replaces the propeller with a gas turbine can go as fast as 265 m.p.h.

A TURBINE-DRIVEN BEHEMOTH

Built to pull two trailers and a total weight of 170,000 pounds, Ford's experimental vehicle, Big Red, recently made a coast-to-coast run in only 77 hours, used a total of 890 gallons of diesel fuel. The turbine's great advantage is concentrated power and smooth operation—since all its parts rotate, the pounding of reciprocating motion is eliminated. But because of problems such as high fuel consumption, inefficient operation at low speeds, and the effect of 950° C. gas temperatures on parts, the turbine is not ready for commercial use.

New Power for
the Big Haulers

Looking for all the world like a flashy new goods train in search of a line to run on, Ford's experimental highway hauler, "Big Red", is shown on the left warming up in a factory lot at Dearborn, Michigan. Under its hood was no ordinary engine, for Big Red was powered by a supercharged gas turbine engine, a compact power unit which produced 600 h.p. without the need of the complex sequence of pistons, crankshafts and clutches of the conventional reciprocating engine. The turbine, like the 1,200-h.p. diesel-electric power plant in the ore truck below, represents the kind of entry needed in the race for brawnier engines to haul heavy cargo, both on the highway and off.

Forty years ago, most deliveries were done by relatively light-weight vehicles. But in the past two decades, a new race of rubber-tyred giants has grown up—30-ton tractor-trailers that can pick up half a wagon load of goods, haul it 3,000 miles and deliver it right to the customer's door. In 1970, about one million petrol and diesel-powered lorries and semi-trailers were moving over 40 per cent of the nation's inter-city freight tonnage, and huge ore trucks hauled some 3,000 million tons of minerals and waste from American mines.

The designers of heavy-duty lorries, far from being satisfied with their progress to date, are now looking beyond Big Red to such advanced power plants as free-piston engines, fuel cells, and possibly even nuclear propulsion to provide greater power and economy for their largest vehicles.

A DIESEL-ELECTRIC MONSTER
This dump lorry, which has a capacity of 100 tons, generates power in its front-mounted diesel engine and transmits it to electric motors in its rear wheels. Such diesel-electric power units were first perfected for goods locomotives; because of their efficiency and flexibility, some transport experts see as bright a future for them on earth-movers and even for trailer-lorries.

A Cargo
for All Carriers

One of the central problems to be solved in any co-ordinated transport system of the future is the transfer of goods from one mode of transportation to another. At present, carrying pieces of cargo by hand from a lorry to a train may cost as much as 75 per cent of the entire freight charge. And the hours spent transferring loads this way may exceed the time it takes the loaded vehicle to get where it is going. One comparatively recent—and highly effective—solution to such bottle-necks is the container (*below*), an outsized metal packing box designed to hold a variety of goods and to move from one carrier to another in a single, quick operation. On the highway, it rolls on a wheel-carriage like a regular semi-trailer; on rails it is

Backing up to a train, a tractor slides one end of a container on to a flat truck (*below, left*). A swivel coupling locks the unit to the truck

secured like a giant crate on a truck.

The container shown here is the increasingly popular large size, a 40-by-8-by-8-foot aluminium unit which may be filled with different kinds of cargo bound for a single destination. After it has been loaded, a truck-tractor pulls the container on its rubber-tyred carriage to the railway yard. There the container drops its car-riage and a yard tractor slides it on to a truck specially designed to receive it. Shipping by container has become so valuable a time- and money-saver that 187,000 of them were in use by 1971. Altogether, some 40 railways, a similar number of air-freight forwarders and a dozen steamship lines are now building or remodelling their carriers to accommodate containers.

(centre), and the wheeled highway carriage is detached. Finally, the tractor swings the other end of the container into place *(right)*.

Special Trains for Bigger Loads

To move more freight with fewer wagons in less time, U.S. railways are building bigger and better cars designed for specialized loads. For still greater efficiency, they are also putting some of the wagons together in strings of single-purpose "unit" trains. These trains—like the unique rail carrier on the right, seen snaking through a gorge in Tennessee—carry one kind of cargo from one point to another and return empty. Unlike trains with mixed cargo and destinations, they make no intermediate stops; this system also dispenses with the shuffling of cars in shunting-yards, and long waits on sidings. On these express routes a unit train can make as many as 150 round trips per year, compared with 18 by a conventional goods train. Running on a 24-hour delivery schedule, one unit train has moved 300,000 brand-new motorcars in six months between Detroit and New York. And unit trains of special wagons carrying up to 110 tons each have proved so efficient that they now move a third of all rail-borne coal in the U.S.

CORN IN THE HOPPER

Corn pours through the pipe (*opposite*) of a Henderson, Kentucky, grain elevator into one of a line of 87-ton hopper cars. Each can be filled in 10 minutes by one man, and unloaded in seven minutes through large outlets in the bottom.

THE LONGEST LOAD

Thirty-two ribbons of welded steel rail, on the right, running the entire length of a 1,440-foot-long work train, head out to be laid on a new section of right-of-way near Brentwood, Tennessee, on the Louisville and Nashville Railway. The heavy rails are cradled on specially designed racks equipped with rollers for easy unloading.

In Europe, De Luxe Service on Rails

As the U.S. moves ahead in devising efficient ways to carry freight by rail, other countries are developing more sophisticated trains for modern passenger transport. The swift German, French and Italian engines that are shown here use automatic control systems and smooth, straight roadbeds to whisk passengers along at cruising speeds up to 125 m.p.h. Taking advantage of cheap hydroelectric power, particularly in Scandinavia and the Alpine countries, other European nations have been electrifying more and more track, so that today Western Europe has an integrated network of some 55,000 miles of electrified lines stretching from the northernmost point in Sweden to the heel of the Italian boot. *En route*, accommodations are more comfortable and the food better than in the U.S., and at the depots European countries provide convenient transfer facilities to buses and lorries that are essential to a co-ordinated system.

RECORD RUNS BY REMOTE CONTROL
Fastest of all the crack new trains in regular service in European passenger lines is the sleek *Blauer Enzian* ("Blue Gentian") of the Deutsche Bundesbahn of Germany (*above*), which hits 125 m.p.h. on its Hamburg-Munich run. Its locomotive is driven by six electric motors with a total output of 12,000 h.p., and can accelerate from zero to top speed in only three minutes. Once the engine is moving at 94 m.p.h., a computer on board takes over the controls, receiving instructions by electronic signal from a traffic control centre.

THE 100-MILE-AN-HOUR PRIDE OF FRANCE
In all Europe there is no more celebrated train than France's *Mistral* (*right*), named after the wind that sweeps south through the Rhone Valley. The prototype for the engine that pulls the *Mistral* between Paris and Marseilles holds the passenger-train speed record—205.6 m.p.h. in a hair-raising test in 1955—but the *Mistral* itself does not exceed 100 m.p.h. on its regular run.

Having slowed for a bend, Italy's *Settebello* ("Seven of Diamonds") speeds to 112 m.p.h. on a straight line to Milan.

The Rails' Answer to the Plane

The hurtling string of railway carriages shown below provides fresh evidence that the ancient concept of the wheel can compete with the aeroplane for a place in the coming scheme of high-speed travel. The train is Japan's electric-powered Shinkansen Express, which regularly covers the 320 miles between Tokyo and Osaka in only 3 hours, 10 minutes. Time for Tokyo-Osaka airline passengers: about 3 hours, including a long battle through car traffic to and from the airports—but not counting take-off and landing delays caused by weather.

The Shinkansen, which began service in 1964 as the Tokaido Express, rolls over welded rails at an average speed of over 100 m.p.h. for the trip. This speed is so fast that the reflexes of a human engineer alone are not thought quick enough to operate the train safely. There are no trackside signal towers, since the speeding train

Working up to a speed of 130 m.p.h., one of the Shinkansen Line's crack trains, *Hikari* (meaning "Light"), streaks across a trestle *en*

would be past the signal and into the danger area before a hand could be put on the brake lever. Instead, the brakes are operated entirely automatically by an electric signal fed in through the rail. The signal is set by two factors: the maximum speed for that section of track, and the nearness of the next train ahead; if the actual speed of a train exceeds the speed indicated by the signal, the brakes are tripped. In its first year of operation, the line carried more than 23 million passengers, and by 1966 it had absorbed more than half the passengers who had previously been required to fly by commercial airline between Tokyo and Osaka. By 1974 the continuing success of the "bullet" trains had sparked a construction programme for a 4,500-mile high-speed rail network that includes a 300-mile extension of the Shinkansen line to Kyushu, the southernmost island.

route to Osaka. TV cameras on the undercarriage monitor wheel bearings for overheating which could lead to a disastrous derailment.

Five Champions among Bridges

A bridge is ranked by the length of its open span—the distance it crosses between supports. Span is the mark of achievement because it usually presents the greatest challenge to the builder: the longer the span stretches— over raging torrents, calm harbours, canyons or canals— the more difficult is the problem of holding the structure up. This challenge has been met in a variety of ways by the bridges sketched below, each the longest of its kind.

CONCRETE ARCH

Built across the river Parramatta at Gladesville, Australia, this bridge of reinforced concrete spans 1,000 feet. The arch owes its great strength to its shape, which directs load stresses outwards from the centre. Slender steel reinforcing rods imbedded in the concrete help carry the forces and make it possible to build an arch that is shallow enough for low approaches.

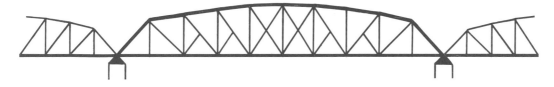

SIMPLE TRUSS

The centre span of this bridge over the river Ohio at Metropolis, Illinois, measures 720 feet. The framework of diagonal steel members along the sides, called trusswork, serves to distribute the stresses of loads from the centre towards the supports at either end. Compared to many other types of bridges, simple truss bridges are easy to design and cheap to construct.

STEEL ARCH

A roadway 1,652 feet long hangs from this arch over the Kill van Kull waterway at Bayonne, New Jersey. A steel arch— usually braced by trusswork—can be considerably longer than a concrete arch because structural steel has remarkable tensile strength; this enables it to resist the enormous stretching forces that are generated by a very long, shallow arch design.

CANTILEVER

Stretching 1,800 feet over the river St. Lawrence at Quebec, the main span of this bridge is designed to give shipping a wide passageway. Two sections, each supported only at the shoreward end, project out over the water, somewhat like diving boards; they hold up a third, smaller section between them. This third section was built on shore, then lifted into place.

SUSPENSION

The longest spans of all are those of suspension bridges, and the world's champion is the 4,260-foot span of the Verrazano-Narrows Bridge, crossing the broad passageway for ships at the mouth of New York Harbor. By hanging the roadway from four cables strung over a pair of towers, the designers of these bridges exploit the tensile strength of steel to the utmost.

A Blend of Systems
for the Motor-Car

A motor-car has a power system that is fuelled by petrol but activated by electricity. These two component systems for power, shown in detail below, work together to make the operation of the engine self-sustaining as well as easily regulated, stopped and restarted. A third system of gears and shafts (*right*) delivers speed and driving force, in adjustable amounts, to the wheels.

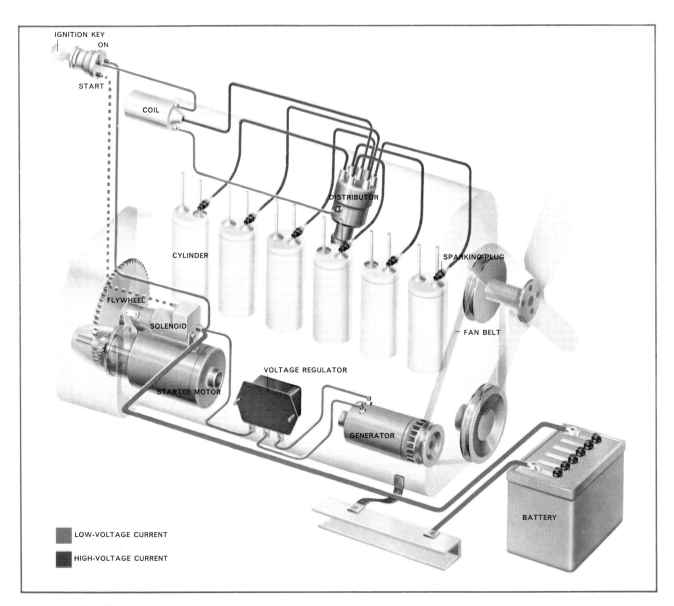

IGNITION KEY
ON
START
COIL
DISTRIBUTOR
CYLINDER
SPARKING-PLUG
FLYWHEEL
SOLENOID
FAN BELT
STARTER MOTOR
VOLTAGE REGULATOR
GENERATOR
BATTERY

LOW-VOLTAGE CURRENT

HIGH-VOLTAGE CURRENT

ELECTRICITY—THE UNSEEN AID

Electricity is indispensable to the operation of a car engine. It activates the starter that gets the engine turning, then fires the fuel that makes the engine run. The process begins at the battery (*lower right*), where electricity is stored. The battery starts dispensing low-voltage current (*light blue*) as soon as the driver turns the key (*top left*) to "start" position. This closes a circuit (*dashed line*) to a device called a solenoid (*lower left*). The solenoid switches on the electrical starter motor after connecting it to the flywheel. The starter motor turns the flywheel; since the flywheel is fastened to the crankshaft of the engine, it forces the pistons to move, thus drawing fuel into the cylinders. At the same time the flywheel also spins the distributor (*top centre*), which with the coil (*top left*), metes out high-voltage current (*dark blue*) to the sparking-plug in each cylinder (*centre*)—as shown in detail on page 80—thus igniting the fuel. When steady operation begins and the ignition key is set to the "on" position, the starter motor disengages and two other devices come into play—the generator and the voltage regulator (*bottom centre*). The generator, turned by the fan belt, produces more electricity. The voltage regulator gauges the electricity in the battery and adjusts the generator output so that the electrical needs of the car are met and the battery is recharged for future starting.

DELIVERING THE POWER

Engine power reaches the wheels by way of a complex sequence of shafts and gears which begins at the crankshaft. The crankshaft converts the up-and-down motion of the pistons to rotary motion, and this turns a set of gears called the transmission, which can increase the driving effort, or torque, at the expense of speed. The power is then carried by the long drive shaft, jointed for flexibility, to the differential, which uses another set of gears to divide up the power and send some to each wheel.

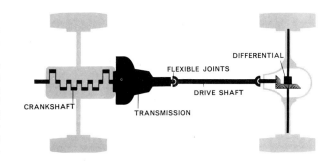

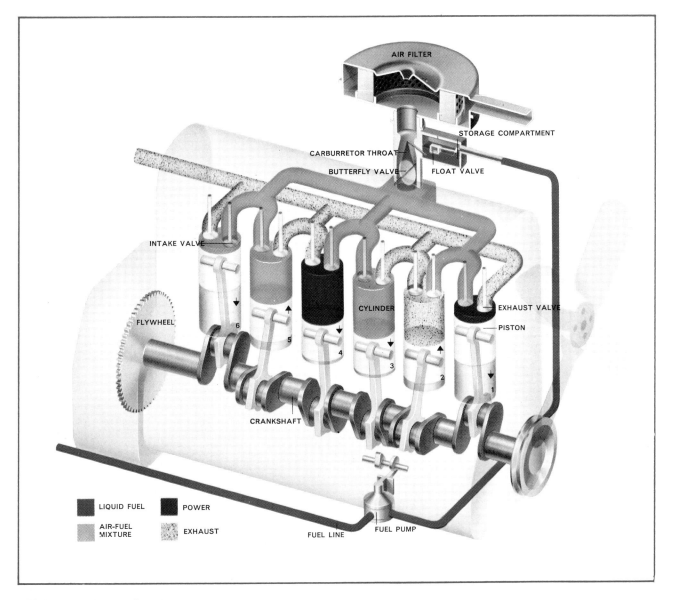

FUEL—THE SOURCE OF POWER

Petrol reaches the cylinders to be converted into driving power only after travelling through a complex of tubes, pipes and valves. The liquid fuel (*medium blue*) arrives from the petrol tank, approaching the engine from the left via the fuel line. A small pump (*bottom*), connected to the crankshaft, forces the fuel up towards the carburettor assembly (*top*). There the petrol enters a storage compartment where a float valve—much like the float valve in a toilet tank—keeps a constant amount available in the compartment. The liquid is sucked into the carburettor by a rushing airstream that is pulled by the moving pistons down through the air filter and carburettor throat. In the carburettor, the wafer-like butterfly valve, controlled by the accelerator pedal of the car, turns to adjust the amount of air-fuel mixture that is supplied. This mixture becomes a gaseous vapour (*light blue*) on its way to the cylinders, where four kinds of stroke—intake, compression, power and exhaust—will convert the fuel into power. In the six-cylinder engine shown here, cylinders 6 and 3 are on the intake stroke, pulling in fuel through their open intake valves; cylinder 5 is on compression, squeezing its fuel charge; cylinders 1 and 4 are on their power strokes, delivering energy from ignited fuel charges (*dark blue*); and cylinder 2 is on exhaust, pushing burned gases (*black*) out through its open exhaust valve.

195

FURTHER READING

Technology

Kirby, Richard, et al., *Engineering in History* (n.e.) McGraw-Hill, 1961.

Klemm, Friedrich, *A History of Western Technology*. Allen & Unwin, 1964.

Singer, Charles, et al., *A History of Technology*, Vols. I-IV. Oxford University Press, 1954-1958.

White, Lynn Jr., *Medieval Technology and Social Change*. Oxford University Press, 1962.

Economics

Fair, Marvin L., and Ernest W. Williams Jr., *Economics of Transportation* (r.e.) Harper & Row, 1959.

Taylor, George Rogers, *Transportation Revolution, 1815-1860* (Vol. IV of *The Economic History of the United States*). Holt, Rinehart & Winston, 1951.

Transportation

Donovan, Frank R., *Wheels for a Nation*. Cromwell, 1965.

Dunbar, Seymour, *A History of Travel in America*. Tudor, 1937.

Gruen, Victor, *The Heart of the City*. Simon & Schuster, 1964.

Halprin, Lawrence, *Freeways*. Holt, Reinhold & Winston, 1966.

Henry, Robert Selph, *This Fascinating Railroad Business*. Bobbs-Merrill, 1946.

Holbrook, Stewart H., *The Story of American Railroads*. Crown, 1947.

Hornung, Clarence P., *Wheels across America*. A. S. Barnes, 1959.

Miller, John A., *Fares, Please!* Dover: Constable, 1960.

†Mumford, Lewis, *The Highway and the City*. Harcourt, 1963, Secker, 1964.

Rae, John B., *The American Automobile; a Brief History*. University of Chicago Press, 1965.

Reck, Franklin M., *The Romance of American Transportation* (r.e.), Cromwell, 1962.

*Stover, John F., *American Railroads*. University of Chicago, 1961.

Roads and Bridges

*Gies, Joseph, *Bridges and Men*. Cassell, 1965.

Oglesby, C. H., and L. I. Hewes, *Highway Engineering* (2nd edition). Wiley, 1963.

Shirley-Smith, H., *The World's Great Bridges* (n.e.). Phoenix House, 1964.

*Steinman, David B., and Sara Ruth Watson, *Bridges and Their Builders*. Dover: Constable, 1941.

*Also available in paperback edition.

†Only available in paperback edition.

ACKNOWLEDGEMENTS

The editors of this book are indebted to the following persons and institutions: American Trucking Assoc., especially John Reith and Edwin H. Spencer, Wash., D.C.; Juergen Arnold, German Federal RR, N.Y.C.; from the Assoc. of American Railroads, Wash., D.C.: Robert Byrne, H. Stephen Dewhurst, Susan Grady, William Henry, Frances M. Meilleur, James Powers and especially W. M. Keller and James N. Sites; from the Automobile Manufacturers Assoc., Detroit: Stanley S. Roe, William F. Sherman, Peter Teeley, Perry L. TeWalt, Harry A. Williams; Ched Bahn, Volkswagen of America, Englewood Cliffs, N.J.; John Barriger, Pres., Missouri-Kansas-Texas RR, St. Louis; George Barris, Barris Kustom City, North Hollywood, Calif.; Dwight M. Baumann, Alexander J. Bone, Siegfried M. Breuning, A. J. Hansen, Charles L. Miller, Walter W. Seifert, M.I.T.; Bell Aerospace Div., Textron, especially Joseph Cannon, Cliff Olivera, Emanuel Paxhia, Buffalo, N.Y.; Donald S. Berry, William L. Garrison, Mary Roy, Technological Institute, Northwestern U., Evanston, Ill.; B&O-C&O RR, H. N. Laden, Baltimore; Bureau of Public Roads, U.S. Dept. of Commerce, especially Edward H. Holmes, Wash., D.C.; Arthur Carney and John Enos, New York Air Brake Co., N.Y.C.; Chevrolet Motor Div. of General Motors Corp., especially Joseph F. Bertsch, Lee R. Bowling, Russell R. Hershberger, Paul Hitch, Leonard Westrate, Detroit; Damon Childs, City Planning Commission, Phila.; D. Gregg Cummings, Electro-Motive Div., General Motors Corp., La Grange, Ill.; U. William Cunitz, William Jordan, William Wilson, New York Central RR, N.Y.C.; Harmer Davis, U. of Calif., Berkeley; Scott Ditch, The Rouse Co., Baltimore; Hall E. Downey, General Railway Signal Co.; L. K. Edwards, Lockheed Missiles and Space Co., Sunnyvale, Calif.; Judith Faghlig, Howard Johnson's, N.Y.C.; Michael Fontanetta and J. Herbert Lund, American Steel Foundries, Chicago; from Ford Motor Co.: Kenneth W. Cunningham, C. A. Freeman, Robert W. Gaines, Charles Gumushian, Hayes Holmes, James Knowles, Gerhard Peitsch, Richard A. Rousos, Dearborn, Mich., and John Cameron, N.Y.C.; Aaron Gellman, North American Car Co., Chicago; General Electric Co., especially Robert L. Falzone, D. H.

McHenry, Russell Smith, Erie, Pa.; General Motors Corp. Truck and Coach Div., especially John A. Castle and Robert E. Field, Pontiac, Mich.; Mel Gooch, Victor Gruen Associates, Los Angeles; Griffin Wheel Co., N.Y.C.; John F. Harris, Fred Pascoe, Barrie T. Smith, Union Switch & Signal, Pittsburgh; Fred N. Hauser and Luther Miller, Simmons-Boardman Publishing Co., N.Y.C.; Shirley Henschel, U.S. Motor Sport Promotions, N.Y.C.; Hank Isbrul, Barnes-Kotler Ford, Brooklyn; Frederick Kilgour, Yale; Norman Klein, Skidmore, Owings & Merrill, San Francisco; Woodson Knight, Louisville and Nashville RR, Louisville, Ky.; Melvin Kranzberg, Case Inst. of Technology, Cleveland; Conrad Lang, New York Thruway, Albany; Pierre Lebris, French Nat. RR, N.Y.C.; Anita Liden, Swedish Info. Service, N.Y.C.; James Martin, Project Coordinator, Redevelopment Authority of the City of Phila.; C. W. McClellan, Fisher Body Corp., Warren, Mich.; Charles Metcalf, Sverdrup & Parcel, Consulting Engineers, N.Y.C.; Everett Miller, Library of Vehicles, Garden Grove, Calif.; H. Gene Miller, Nat. Safety Council, Chicago; R. W. Mutch, Conference of European Railways, N.Y.C.; Robert Nelson, Dept. of Commerce, Wash., D.C.; Thomas Norrell, Silver Spring, Md.; Pennsylvania RR, especially William Baird, Pittsburgh, and Robert Rutledge, Conway, Pa.; E. Grosvenor Plowman, Portland, Me.; M. D. Post, Bethlehem Steel Corp., Bethlehem, Pa.; Frank Rowsome Jr., Wash., D.C.; Runzheimer and Co., Runzheimer Park, Rochester, Wis.; Michael Ruvolo, Automotive High School, Brooklyn; Nettie Seabrooks, General Motors Corp., Detroit; Irene Simpson, Wells Fargo Bank, San Francisco; Frank A. Smith, Transportation Assoc. of America, Wash., D.C.; Southern Railway System, Wash., D.C.; George F. Stevenson, Louisiana Dept. of Highways, Baton Rouge, La.; Gilbert Sweet, Atchison, Topeka and Santa Fe Railway Co., Chicago; George Tedesco, Pullman, Chicago; Union Pacific RR, Barry Combs and Edwin C. Schafer, Omaha; Robert Vogel and Jack White, Smithsonian Institution, Wash., D.C.; Kenneth Vore, U.S. Steel, Pittsburgh; Westinghouse Air Brake Co., N.Y.C. and Wilmerding, Pa.; Roman Wolchuk, N.Y.C.

INDEX

Numerals in italics indicate a photograph or painting of the subject mentioned.

199

PICTURE CREDITS

The sources for the illustrations which appear in this book are shown below. Credits for the pictures from left to right are separated by commas, from top to bottom by dashes.

CHAPTER 1: 8—Jack Birns. 12, 14—Drawings by Leslie Martin. 17—Loomis Dean. 18, 19—Henri Cartier-Bresson from Magnum—Robert Crandall courtesy The Metropolitan Museum of Art. 20, 21—Al Mellett from Magnum—Larry Burrows courtesy The Karachi Museum. 22, 23—Left Universitets Oldsaksamling, Oslo; right courtesy The British Museum—Leonard McCombe. 24, 25—Erich Lessing from Magnum, Al Mellett from Magnum. 26, 27—Left from The Eugene Fuller Memorial Collection courtesy The Seattle Art Museum; right Loomis Dean—Bradley Smith. 28, 29—Carl Mydans.

CHAPTER 2: 30—Erich Lessing from Magnum. 32—The Bettmann Archive. 34—From "*Life of Richard Trevithick*" by Francis Trevithick, Vol. I, p. 181, published by E. & F. N. Spon, 1872. 36—The Science Museum, London. 37—Drawing by John and Mary Condon. 39—Robert Crandall courtesy Continental Insurance. 40, 41—Robert Crandall courtesy Columbia University. 42, 43—Robert Crandall courtesy the Albany Institute of History and Art. 44, 45—British Crown Copyright The Science Museum, London, Frank Lerner courtesy Columbia University Libraries, Henry B. Beville courtesy The Smithsonian Institution on loan from Mrs. Thomas Norrell, Henry B. Beville courtesy The Smithsonian Institution—British Crown Copyright The Science Museum, London, Frank Lerner courtesy Columbia University Libraries, Frank Lerner courtesy The Coverdale and Colpitts Collection—The Science Museum, London, Frank Lerner courtesy Columbia University Libraries, Henry B. Beville courtesy The Smithsonian Institution. 46—Frank Lerner. 47—Library of Congress—Culver Pictures Inc. 48—Baltimore and Ohio Railroad—New York Central Railroad—Santa Fe Railway. 49—Frank Lerner courtesy The New York Historical Society—Santa Fe Railway—Baltimore and Ohio Railroad. 50, 51—New York Central Systems.

CHAPTER 3: 52—David Plowden from Rapho Guillumette courtesy Stephen Greene. 54 to 57—Drawings by John and Mary Condon. 58—The Bettmann Archive. 63 to 75—Drawings by Matt Greene except 72 and 73—Matt Greene and James Alexander.

CHAPTER 4: 76—Robert Phillips. 78—Drawings by John and Mary Condon courtesy General Motors Corp. 80, 82, 83—Drawings by Leslie Martin. 84, 85—Drawings by Matt Greene. 87—Arthur Seller—chart by Otto van Eersel. 88, 89—Map drawn by George V. Kelvin photographed by Robert Phillips; symbols and chart by Otto van Eersel. 90—James Burke—chart by Otto van Eersel. 91—Walter Sanders—chart by Otto van Eersel. 92, 93—Photograph by Arthur Seller; right courtesy Ford Motor Company—chart by Otto van Eersel. 94, 95—

Charts by Otto van Eersel. 96 to 99—Photographs by Arthur Seller, drawings by Otto van Eersel.

CHAPTER 5: 100—Margaret Bourke-White. 102—Drawings by John and Mary Condon. 104—Drawings by John and Mary Condon. 109—Herbert Loebel. 110, 111—Guy Gillette for FORTUNE, Henry Grossman. 112, 113—J. R. Eyerman. 114, 115—Henry Grossman (2), Wayne Miller from Magnum. 116, 117—Arthur Rickerby. 118, 119—George Silk, Robert Phillips—Richard Meek for SPORTS ILLUSTRATED, Art Kane. 120, 121—Fred Schnell.

CHAPTER 6: 122—Peter Stackpole. 124—Culver Pictures Inc. 125—From *Peru* by E. George Squire, p. 558, Harper and Brothers, 1877. 127—From *Scientific American*, April 15, 1871. 128, 129—From *Scientific American*, November 12, 1870 courtesy The New York Public Library. 133—Andreas Feininger. 134, 135—Margaret Bourke-White, Laenderpress, Düsseldorf. 136, 137—Foto Locci—Foto Vasari, Rome, Max Bill, Zürich. 138—A. Y. Owen. 139—René Vital for *Paris-Match*. 140, 141—Robert W. Kelley, Joe Munroe for TIME (2). 142, 143—Ted Spiegel from Rapho Guillumette for TIME—Peter Fischer, Cologne. 144—Joern Gerdts.

CHAPTER 7: 146—Courtesy the Museum of the City of New York and the Bettmann Archive. 148—The Bettmann Archive. 151—From *Electrical World*, September 25, 1886 figs. 3 and 4. 155—Drawing by Gloria Cernosia. 157 to 167—Drawings by Victor Lazzaro except 166 left drawing by John and Mary Condon. 157, 160, 161—Courtesy of Skidmore, Owings and Merrill, San Francisco, and the Redevelopment Authority of the City of Philadelphia. 158, 159—Courtesy The Louisiana Department of Highways. 162, 163—Courtesy Victor Gruen Associates, Los Angeles. 164, 165—Courtesy the Swedish Information Service, New York. 166, 167—Courtesy the Rouse Co., Baltimore.

CHAPTER 8: 168—*Business Week* photo by Richard Knapp. 170—Chart by Gloria Cernosia. 173—Drawing by Donald and Ann Crews. 175—Drawing by John and Mary Condon. 176—Drawing by Donald and Ann Crews. 179—Derek Bayes courtesy Peel Engineering Ltd., Isle of Man. 180, 181—Ted Streshinsky. 182, 183—Bill Ray, Unit Rig and Equipment Co. 184, 185—Robert Phillips. 186—Bruce Roberts from Rapho Guillumette. 187—Louisville and Nashville Railroad Co. 188, 189—Top right Ferrovie Italiane Dello Stato; bottom left Deutsche Bundesbahn Bildarchiv; centre Images et Textes Laforgerie. 190, 191—JNR. 193—Drawings by Donald and Ann Crews. 194, 195—Drawings by George V. Kelvin.

Typesetting by C. E. Dawkins (Typesetters) Ltd., London, SE1 1UN
Smeets Lithographers, Weert, Printed in Holland
Bound by Proost en Brandt N.V., Amsterdam